W9-CSM-582

Essentials of the US Health Care System

Leiyu Shi, DrPH, MBA
Associate Professor
Department of Health Policy Management
School of Hygiene and Public Health
Johns Hopkins University
Baltimore, Maryland

Douglas A. Singh, PhD, MBA
Associate Professor
School of Public and
Environmental Affairs
Indiana University
South Bend, Indiana

JONES AND BARTLETT PUBLISHERS
Sudbury, Massachusetts
BOSTON   TORONTO   LONDON   SINGAPORE

World Headquarters
Jones and Bartlett Publishers
40 Tall Pine Drive
Sudbury, MA 01776
978-443-5000
info@jbpub.com
www.jbpub.com

Jones and Bartlett Publishers Canada
6339 Ormindale Way
Mississauga, ON L5V 1J2
CANADA

Jones and Bartlett Publishers International
Barb House, Barb Mews
London W6 7PA
UK

Jones and Bartlett's books and products are available through most bookstores and online booksellers. To contact Jones and Bartlett Publishers directly, call 800-832-0034, fax 978-443-8000, or visit our website at www.jbpub.com.

Substantial discounts on bulk quantities of Jones and Bartlett's publications are available to corporations, professional associations, and other qualified organizations. For details and specific discount information, contact the special sales department at Jones and Bartlett via the above contact information or send an email to specialsales@jbpub.com.

ISBN-13: 978-0-7637-3886-0
ISBN-10: 0-7637-3886-7

6048

Printed in the United States of America

10 09 08 07 06   10 9 8 7 6 5 4 3 2

Contents

How This Book Can Help You Learn

All of us have different learning styles. Some of us are visual learners, some more auditory, some learn better by doing an activity. Some students prefer to learn new material using visual aids. Some learn material better when they hear it in a lecture; others learn it better by reading it. Cognitive research has shown that no matter what your learning style, you will learn more if you are actively engaged in the learning process.

This Student Note-Taking Guide will help you learn by providing a structure to your notes and letting you utilize all of the learning styles mentioned above. Students don't need to copy down every word their professor says or recopy their entire textbook. Do the assigned reading, listen in lecture, follow the key points your instructor is making, and write down meaningful notes. After reading and lectures, review your notes and pull out the most important points.

The Student Note-Taking Guide is your partner and guide in note-taking. Your Guide provides you with a visual guide that follows the chapter topics presented in your textbook. If your instructor is using the PowerPoint slides that accompany the text, this guide will save you from having to write down everything that is on the slides. There is space provided for you to jot down the terms and concepts that you feel are most important to each lecture. By working with your Guide, you are seeing, hearing, writing, and, later, reading and reviewing. The more often you are exposed to the material, the better you will learn and understand it. Using different methods of exposure significantly increases your comprehension.

Your Guide is the perfect place to write down questions that you want to ask your professor later, interesting ideas that you want to discuss with your study group, or reminders to yourself to go back and study a certain concept again to make sure that you really got it.

Having organized notes is essential at exam time and when doing homework assignments. Your ability to easily locate the important concepts of a recent lecture will help you move along more rapidly, as you don't have to spend time rereading an entire chapter just to reinforce one point that you may not have quite understood.

Your Guide is a valuable resource. You've found a wonderful study partner!

Note-Taking Tips

1. It is easier to take notes if you are not hearing the information for the first time. Read the chapter or the material that is about to be discussed before class. This will help you to anticipate what will be said in class, and have an idea of what to write down. It will also help to read over your notes from the last class. This way you can avoid having to spend the first few minutes of class trying to remember where you left off last time.
2. Don't waste your time trying to write down everything that your professor says. Instead, listen closely and only write down the important points. Review these important points after class to help remind you of related points that were made during the lecture.
3. If the class discussion takes a spontaneous turn, pay attention and participate in the discussion. Only take notes on the conclusions that are relevant to the lecture.
4. Emphasize main points in your notes. You may want to use a highlighter, special notation (asterisks, exclamation points), format (circle, underline), or placement on the page (indented, bulleted). You will find that when you try to recall these points, you will be able to actually picture them on the page.
5. Be sure to copy down word-for-word specific formulas, laws, and theories.
6. Hearing something repeated, stressed, or summed up can be a signal that it is an important concept to understand.
7. Organize handouts, study guides, and exams in your notebook along with your lecture notes. It may be helpful to use a three-ring binder, so that you can insert pages wherever you need to.
8. When taking notes, you might find it helpful to leave a wide margin on all four sides of the page. Doing this allows you to note names, dates, definitions, etc. for easy access and studying later. It may also be helpful to make notes of questions you want to ask your professor about or research later, ideas or relationships that you want explore more on your own, or concepts that you don't fully understand.
9. It is best to maintain a separate notebook for each class. Labeling and dating your notes can be helpful when you need to look up information from previous lectures.
10. Make your notes legible, and take notes directly in your notebook. Chances are you won't recopy them no matter how noble your intentions. Spend the time you would have spent recopying the notes studying them instead, drawing conclusions and making connections that you didn't have time for in class.
11. Look over your notes after class while the lecture is still fresh in your mind. Fix illegible items and clarify anything you don't understand. Do this again right before the next class.

Notes

Chapter 1

Major Characteristics
of
U.S. Health Care
Delivery

Introduction

- The United States has a unique system of health care delivery.

- The US health care delivery system is complex and massive.

Introduction

- "Health care delivery" and "health services delivery"

  - Can have slightly different meanings, but in a broad sense, both terms refer to the:

    - major components of the system

    - processes that enable people to receive health care.

    - provision of health care services to patients.

Introduction

- In contrast to the United States,

  - ◆ most developed countries have national health insurance programs

    - ★ referred to as "universal access"

      - • provide routine and basic health care
      - • run by the government and financed through general taxes.

  - ◆ All Americans are <u>not</u> "entitled" to routine and basic health care services.

Introduction

- 187.4 million Americans have private health insurance coverage,
  - ★ 35.2 million Medicare beneficiaries, and
  - ★ 31.5 million Medicaid recipients.
- Health insurance can be bought from:
  - ◆ 1,000 health insurance companies
  - ◆ 70 BlueCross/BlueShield plans
- The managed care sector includes approximately:
  - ◆ 540 licensed health maintenance organizations (HMOs)
  - ◆ 925 preferred provider organizations (PPOs)

Subsystems of US Health Care Delivery

- Managed Care

- Military

- Vulnerable Populations

- Integrated Delivery

Subsystems of
US Health Care Delivery

Managed Care

- ◆ A system of health care delivery that:

  1) seeks to achieve efficiency by integrating the basic functions of healthcare delivery
  2) employs mechanisms to control (manage) utilization of medical services
  3) determines the price at which the services are purchased and how much the providers get paid.

Subsystems of
US Health Care Delivery

- ■ Managed Care

  - ◆ Is the most dominant health care delivery system in the United States and available to most Americans.
  - ◆ Employers and government are the primary financiers of managed care
  - ◆ An MCO functions like
    - • an insurance company
      - – it promises to provide health care services contracted under the health plan to the enrollees of the plan.

Subsystems of
US Health Care Delivery

- ■ Managed Care
  - ◆ Enrollee refers to:
    - ★ a member
    - ★ an individual covered under the plan
  - ◆ Health plan:
    - ★ a contractual arrangement between the MCO and the enrollee
      - • includes a list of covered health services to which enrollees are entitled
    - ★ uses selected providers
      - • usually primary care, general practioners
        --the "gatekeepers"

      - • Look at Figure 1.1, page 5

Subsystems of US Health Care Delivery

Military

- ◆ The military medical care system is available free of charge to:

    - ★ active duty military personnel of the U.S. Army, Navy, Air Force, and Coast Guard,

    - ★ certain uniformed nonmilitary services such as
        - the Public Health Services and
        - the National Oceanographic and Atmospheric Association (NOAA)

Subsystems of US Health Care Delivery

Military

- ◆ The military medical care system is

    - ★ well-organized

    - ★ highly integrated

    - ★ comprehensive
        - covers preventative care

Subsystems of US Health Care Delivery

Military

- ◆ TRICARE

    - ★ Financed by the military, and covers families, dependents or retired military

Subsystems of
US Health Care Delivery

Military

- The VA health care system

  - available to retired veterans

  - focuses on
    - hospital, mental health and long-term care

  - Is one of the largest and oldest (1946) organized health systems in the world

Subsystems of
US Health Care Delivery

Military

The mission of the VA health care system:

- Provide medial care, education and training, research, contingency support and emergency management for the Department of Defense medical care system.

Subsystems of
US Health Care Delivery

Military

- The VA health care system has:

    - over 1,100 sites
    - 172 hospitals
    - 206 counseling centers
    - 40 residential care facilities
    - 73 home health programs, and

    - provides care to 3.6 million

Notes

_____

_____

_____

_____

_____

_____

_____

_____

_____

_____

_____

_____

_____

_____

_____

_____

_____

_____

_____

_____

_____

_____

_____

_____

_____

_____

_____

_____

_____

_____

_____

_____

_____

_____

_____

_____

_____

_____

_____

_____

_____

_____

_____

_____

_____

_____

_____

Subsystems of US Health Care Delivery
Military
■ The VA:
◆ Budgets over $20 billion
◆ Employs over 182,000
◆ Affiliates with
★ 13,000 physicians
★ 53,000 nurses
★ 3,500 pharmacists

Subsystems of US Health Care Delivery
Military
■ The VA is:
◆ organized into 22 geographically-distributed Veterans Integrated Service Networks (VISN)
• Each VISN
– coordinates its own services
– receives federal funds

Subsystems of US Health Care Delivery
Vulnerable Populations
◆ Particularly the poor, uninsured, minorities and immigrants
★ live in disadvantaged communities and receive care from "safety net" providers.

Subsystems of US Health Care Delivery

Vulnerable Populations

◆ Safety nets are not secure

★ Provider type and availability vary
★ Some individuals forego care and seek hospital emergency services if nearby
★ Providers pressured to see the rising number of uninsureds
★ Medicaid, the primary financial source for the safety net, does not allow much cost shifting

Subsystems of US Health Care Delivery

Integrated Delivery

■ The hallmark of the US health care industry:
  ★ to form integrated delivery systems (IDS)

■ IDS
  ◆ are various forms of ownership and links among hospitals, physicians and insurers

  ◆ IDS' objective:
    ★ To have one health care organization deliver a range of services

Subsystems of US Health Care Delivery

Integrated Delivery

■ IDS is

  ◆ A network of organizations that provides or arranges to provide a coordinated continuum of services to

    – defined populations held clinically and fiscally accountable for outcomes and health status

Notes

Characteristics Of The U.S. Health Care System

- No Central Governing Agency;
    - Little Integration and Coordination
- Technology-Driven and Focuses on Acute Care
- High on cost, Unequal in Access, and Average in Outcomes
- Imperfect Market Conditions
- Government as Subsidiary to the Private Sector
- Market Justice vs. Social Justice
- Multiple Players and Balance of Power
- Quest for Integration and Accountability

Characteristics Of The U.S. Health Care System

- No Central Governing Agency;
    - Little Integration and Coordination
    - The US system is different from other developed countries
        - It is not centrally-controlled
            - Central systems are less complex, less costly
        - Has different payment, insurance, and delivery mechanisms
        - Health care is financed both publicly and privately
            - Look at Exhibit 1.1, page 8

Characteristics Of The U.S. Health Care System

- Technology-Driven and Focuses on Acute Care

    - The US invests in research and innovations in new medical technology

    - Growth in science and technology helps create demand for new services, despite shrinking resources to finance sophisticated care

Characteristics of The U.S. Health Care System

- Technology-Driven and Focuses on Acute Care
  - ◆ Technology has had successful interventions, but is overused
    - This prohibits
      - employers extending benefits to part-time workers and
      - insurers lowering premiums

Characteristics Of The U.S. Health Care System

- High on Cost, Unequal in Access, and Average in Outcome

- The United States spends more than any other developed country on health care

  - ◆ Costs continue to rise at an alarming rate.

  - ◆ Many have limited access to basic care

Characteristics Of The U.S. Health Care System

- High on Cost, Unequal in Access, and Average in Outcome

  - ◆ Access

    - ★ The ability of an individual to obtain health care services when needed

Notes

Characteristics Of The U.S. Health Care System

- High on Cost, Unequal in Access, and Average in Outcome
  - ◆ Access
    - ★ Is restricted in the US to those who:
      1. Have health insurance through an employer
      2. Are covered under a government program
      3. Can afford to buy insurance out-of-pocket
      4. Are able to pay for services privately

Characteristics Of The U.S. Health Care System

- High on Cost, Unequal in Access, and Average in Outcome

  - ◆ The absence of insurance inhibits a patient's ability to receive well-directed, coordinated, and continuous care to primary and specialty services if referred.

Characteristics Of The U.S. Health Care System

- Imperfect Market Conditions

  - ◆ Under national health care programs,

    - ★ patients have varying degrees of choice in selecting providers

    - ★ true "free market" forces are virtually nonexistent.

Notes

Characteristics Of The U.S. Health Care System

- Imperfect Market Conditions

  ◆ In a free market,

    ★ multiple patients (buyers) and providers (sellers) act independently.

    ★ patients should be able to choose their provider based on price and quality

Characteristics Of The U.S. Health Care System

- Imperfect Market Conditions

  ◆ For the health care market to be free,

    ★ unrestrained competition must occur among providers, on the basis of price and quality

Characteristics Of The U.S. Health Care System

- Imperfect Market Conditions

  ◆ A free market requires that patients have

    ★ information about the availability of various services

Characteristics Of The U.S. Health Care System

- Imperfect Market Conditions

  ◆ In a free market, patients as consumers must:

    ★ directly bear the cost of services received.

    ★ make decisions about the purchase of health care services

---

Characteristics Of The U.S. Health Care System

- Government as Subsidiary to the Private Sector

  ◆ In most developed countries,
    • government plays a central role in the provision of health care.
  ◆ In the US,
    • the private sector plays the dominant role because of American tradition, and the desire to limit government

---

Characteristics Of The U.S. Health Care System

- Market Justice and Social Justice: Conflict Throughout Health Care

  ◆ Market justice and social justice are:

    ★ two contrasting theories that govern the production and distribution of health care services in the United States.

Characteristics Of The U.S. Health Care System

Multiple Players and Balance of Power

★ The key system players have been:

- physicians
- administrators of health care institutions
- insurance companies
- large employers
- government

Characteristics Of The U.S. Health Care System

■ Quest for integration and accountability

★ In the U.S., there is:

• a drive to use primary care as the organizing hub for continuous and coordinated health services with seamless delivery

★ Accountability

• ethically providing quality health care in an efficient manner
• safeguarding one's own health and using resources sensibly

Health Care Systems Of Other Developed Countries

■ Most western Europe has universal access

◆ Models for national health systems:

1. National Health Insurance

2. National Health System

3. Socialized Health Insurance System

★ Look at Table 1.1, page 16

Notes

_____

_____

_____

_____

_____

_____

_____

_____

_____

_____

_____

_____

_____

_____

_____

_____

_____

_____

_____

_____

_____

_____

_____

_____

_____

_____

_____

_____

_____

_____

_____

_____

_____

_____

Health Care Systems Of Other Developed Countries

- National Health Insurance
  - ★ Canada uses this system

  - ◆ Core of care delivered by private providers

  - ◆ Tighter consolidation of the financing, coordinated by government

---

Health Care Systems Of Other Developed Countries

- National Health Systems
  - ★ Great Britain uses this system

  - ◆ finance a tax-supported national health insurance program:
    - ★ government manages the infrastructure for the delivery of medical care
    - ★ most medical institutions are operated by government
    - ★ most providers are government employees

Health Care Systems Of Other Developed Countries

Socialized Health Insurance Systems

- ★ Germany uses this style
- ◆ Health care is financed through government-mandated contributions by employers and employees
- ◆ Health care delivered by private providers
- ◆ Sickness funds collect and pay for services
- ◆ Insurance and payment is closely integrated
- ◆ Delivery characterized by independent, private arrangements
- ◆ Government exercises overall control

Systems Framework

Systems consist of:

a set of interrelated and interdependent
components designed to achieve some
common goals

Systems Framework

The systems framework:

♦ explains the structure of health care services
in the U.S. based on the foundations

♦ provides a logical arrangement of various
components

♦ demonstrates a progression from inputs to
outputs

Systems Framework

The framework outlines:
♦ System Foundations
♦ System Resources
♦ System Processes
♦ System Outcomes
♦ System Outlook

★ Look at Figure 1.2, page 18

Notes

_____

_____

_____

_____

_____

_____

_____

_____

_____

_____

_____

_____

_____

_____

_____

_____

_____

_____

_____

_____

_____

_____

_____

_____

_____

_____

_____

_____

_____

_____

_____

_____

_____

_____

_____

_____

_____

Conclusion

- The U.S. has a unique system of delivery, therefore
  - ★ continuous and comprehensive care is not enjoyed by all Americans
  - ★ it's a patchwork of subsystems
  - ◆ No country has a perfect system

- The Systems Framework is an
  - ◆ organized approach to understanding the components of the US health care delivery system

Notes

Chapter 2

Foundation of
US Health
Care Delivery

Beliefs, Values and Health

- Curative medicine has
  - decreasing returns in health improvement
    with increased health care expenditures

- There is recognition of the benefits to
  society from the promotion of health and
  prevention

Beliefs, Values and Health

- Beliefs and values in US

  - have remained mostly private,
    - not a tax-financed national health care
      program

  - are strong forces against
    - fundamental changes in the financing and
      delivery of health care

- Social norms explain
  - how we view illness and expectations

What Is Health ?

U.S. health care has followed a medical/biomedical model

 – It presupposes the existence of illness or disease

 – It emphasizes

  • clinical diagnosis and medical interventions to:
   – treat disease or its symptoms

   – have a clinical diagnosis and medical interventions

What Is Health ?

• Absence of illness and disease

• Optimum health exists when
 – a person is free of symptoms and
 – does not require medical treatment

What Is Health ?

• " A state of physical and mental well-being that facilitates the achievements of individual and societal goals"
 – Society for Academic Medicine

• " A complete state of physical, mental and social well being, not merely the absence of disease
 – WHO

  • referred to as the biopsychosocial model of health
  • WHO defined a health care system as
   – all the activities whose primary purpose is to promote, restore, or maintain health

Holistic Health

- Holistic medicine
  - treats the whole person
  - incorporates alternative therapies

- Holistic health incorporates
  - physical, mental, social and spiritual aspects

- Literature shows that:

  - religious & spiritual belief has a positive impact on overall well-being
  - it affects the incidence, experience, and outcomes of common medical problems

Illness vs. Disease

- Illness
  - identified by a person's perception and evaluation of how he/she is feeling

  - people are ill when they
    - infer a diminished capacity to perform tasks and roles expected by society

- Disease
  - based on a professional evaluation
  - requires therapeutic intervention

Disease Classifications

A) <u>acute</u>
  - relatively severe,
  - episodic (of short duration) and
  - often treatable
    - (i.e., myocardial infarct, lack of kidney function)

B) <u>subacute</u>
  - some acute features
  - postacute treatment after discharge
    - (i.e., head trauma, ventilator)

C) <u>chronic</u>
  - less severe, but long and continuous
  - can be controlled, but can lead to serious complications
    - (i.e., asthma, diabetes, hypertension)

Quality of Life

- Overall satisfaction with life during and following a person's encounter with the health care delivery system
- An indicator of how satisfied a person was with the experiences while receiving health care
  - comfort, respect, privacy, security, autonomy
- A person's overall satisfaction with life and self-perceptions of health, especially after a medical intervention
- Goal:
  - have a positive effect on an individual's ability to function, meet obligations, feeling of self-worth

Determinants of Health

Factors that influence an individual and a population's health:
- A person's genetic make up
  - 20% of premature deaths
- Individual Behaviors
  - 50% of premature deaths
- Medical Practice
  - 10%
- Social and Environmental Factors
  - 20%

  - See Figure 2-1

Determinants of Health

- Environment
  - Physical, social, cultural, and economic factors
- Behavior/Lifestyle
  - Diet and foods play a major role in most significant health problems
- Heredity
  - Predisposes individuals to certain diseases
  - Current lifestyles can impact future progeny
- Medical care
  - Access to adequate preventive and curative health care services

Healthy People 2010

- 10 year plans
- key national health objectives
- founded on the integration of medical care and prevention, health promotion and education
- emphasizes the role of community partners
  - (businesses, governments, civic, professional, and religious organizations)
    - as agents for improving health in their communities
- under the US Surgeon General's direction

  - Look at Figure 2-2

Healthy People 2010

Designed to achieve two goals:

1. Increase Quality and Years of Healthy Life

2. Eliminate Health Disparities

Social and Market Justice Approaches

- The production, distribution, and, consumption of health care must be perceived as equitable.

- No society
  - has a perfectly equitable method to distribute limited resources

- Any method of resource distribution leaves some inequalities

Notes

_____
_____
_____
_____
_____
_____
_____
_____
_____
_____
_____
_____
_____
_____
_____
_____
_____
_____
_____
_____
_____
_____
_____
_____
_____
_____
_____
_____
_____
_____
_____
_____
_____
_____
_____
_____

Social and Market Justice Approaches

- A theory of justice is
  - needed to resolve the allocation of health care

- Equitable access to health services is addressed by
  - the theories of market and social justice.

- These two contrasting theories govern
  - the production and distribution of health care services.

Market Justice "The Economic Good"

Fair distribution of health care to the market forces in a free economy

- Medical services distributed on the basis of people's willingness and ability to pay.

Principles of Market Justice

- Health care is
  - an economic good
    - governed by free market forces

- Individuals are
  - responsible for their own achievements

- People make rational choices
  - in their decision to buy health care products and services

Principles of Market Justice

- People consult with their physicians, who know what is best for them

- The market works best without interference from government

Market Justice

- The production of health care is determined by
  - how much the consumers are willing and able to buy at the prevailing price.

- Those not able to pay have barriers to health care
  - "rationing by ability to pay"

- Focus on individual rather than a collective responsibility for health

  - Look at Table 2-1

Social Justice
"The Good Society"

- Theory is at odds with capitalism and market justice

- The equitable distribution of health care is society's responsibility
  - Best when a central agency is responsible for the production and distribution of health care

- Health care is a social good
  - Should be collectively financed and available to every citizen.

Principles of Social Justice

- Health care should be based on need rather than cost

- There is a shared responsibility for health
  - Factors outside a person's control might have brought on the condition

- There is an obligation to the collective good
  - The well-being of the community is superior to that of the individual

Principles of Social Justice

Government, rather than the market, can better decide, through planning,
  - how much health care to provide and how to distribute among all citizens

Social Justice

Planned rationing, supply-side rationing, or nonprice rationing is where

  - government limits the supply of health care services, particularly those beyond the basic level of care

  - Look at Table 2-1

Limitations of Market Justice

- Fails to rectify human concerns such as
  - crime, illiteracy, and homelessness, which can significantly weaken the fabric of a society.
- Does not always protect the society.
- Individual health issues can have negative consequences for society
- Does not work well in health care delivery

Focusing on Determinants

To improve the nation's health and resolve disparities among its vulnerable populations,

- a framework embodying the social and medical determinants is warranted.

  - Look at Figure 2.3

Social Determinants of Health

- The framework includes:
  - demographics, personal behaviors, and community-level inequalities and their defining influence on health.

- Personal demographics
  - (e.g., race/ethnicity or age)
    - directly contribute to vulnerability levels

- Social and income inequalities
  - have shown to contribute to disparities in health

Medical Care Determinants

- The medical care system focuses primarily on treating illness or poor health

- This framework includes:
  - a broad spectrum of medical care services and interventions to improve health,
    - though preventive and primary care
    - contributes to the general health status
      - others are more influential in end-of-life mortality
        » (specialty and long-term care)

Social and Medical Points of Intervention

- Reductions in health disparities are obtainable through interventions

- Interventions are grouped according to four strategies:
  1) social or medical care policy
  2) community-based interventions
  3) health care interventions
  4) individual interventions

1. Social and Medical Points of Intervention

Policy Interventions

- Social or public policy affects the health of the population

- Guards the welfare of the nation

1. Social and Medical Points of Intervention

- **Vulnerable populations**
  - are uniquely dependent upon social and public policy to
    - develop and implement programs that address basic nutritional, safety, social, and health care needs

- **Policy initiatives can be**
  - prevention strategies to alter the dynamics linking social factors to poor health

2. Community-Based Interventions

- **Many health disparities may be addressed at the community or local levels.**

- **Neighborhood poverty, the presence of local health and social welfare resources, and societal cohesion and support contribute to the level of inequalities in a community**

2. Community-Based Interventions

- **Community partnerships**
  - reflect the priorities of a local population
  - are often managed by members of the community
  - minimize cultural barriers
  - improve community buy-in to the program

- **Mobilizing resources at the local level to address problems**

Notes

2. Community-Based Interventions

- Community resources can be applied directly to community members
  - businesses have greater incentive to contribute to local health causes.

- Community solutions benefit from participatory decision making

3. Health Care Interventions

- Designed to
  - improve the quality and efficiency of services provided, and
  - reduce disparities across groups
- Examples include:
  - integrated electronic medical record systems to coordinate care for populations with multiple chronic and acute conditions
  - continuing education for pediatricians to target developmental services to children
  - educating pregnant mothers to receive regular prenatal care

4. Individual-level Interventions

- Attempts to intervene and minimize the effects of negative social determinants on health status.

- Altering behaviors that influence health is often the focus of these individual-level interventions
  - (e.g., reduce smoking and encourage exercise)

Conclusion

- **The health care delivery system in the United States is:**
  - mostly private
    - many of the peculiarities of this system can be traced back to the beliefs and values underlying the American culture
  - driven by the medical model, which emphasizes illness rather than wellness

Conclusion

- **Holistic concepts of health care, along with preventive and health promotional efforts, need to be adopted to significantly improve the health of Americans**

- **It would also require**
  - individual responsibility for one's behaviors
  - community partnerships
  - initiatives such as Healthy People 2010

Conclusion

To improve the nation's health and resolve disparities,
  - it is critical to address both the social and medical determinants of health.

Notes

Notes

Chapter 3

Historical
Overview of
U.S. Health
Care Delivery

Introduction

This chapter will discuss

- the main historical developments that have shaped the health care delivery system in the United States.

Introduction

Historical factors that have shaped the U.S. health care delivery system:

- cultural beliefs,
- values,
- technological advances,
- social changes,
- economic constraints and
- political opportunism
  - Look at Exhibit 3-1, page 46

Introduction

- U.S. health care is therefore mainly a private industry,
  - but receives a large amount of government financing
    - Government mostly finances health care for the poor
    - Middle class must depend on private insurance

- American capitalism
  - promoted entrepreneurship and innovation

Medical Services In Preindustrial America

- The practice of medicine in the Unites States was domestic rather than professional because
  - medical procedures were primitive

- Medical education was not grounded in science

- Medical practice was more a trade than profession

Medical Services In Preindustrial America

- The nation only had a few hospitals
  - they existed in very large cities.

- There was no private or public health insurance

- For characteristics of health care delivery during preindustrial America:
  - look at Exhibit 3.2, page 48

Medical Services
In Preindustrial America

- Medical Training

- Medical Practice

- Medical Institutions

Medical Services
In Preindustrial America

- Medical Training

  – Until about 1870, medical training was largely received through an individual apprenticeship with a practicing physician rather than through a university

  – It was a two-year Doctor of Medicine degree

  – There were only about 42 such schools in 1850

Medical Services
In Preindustrial America

- Medical Training

  – To train a larger number of students than was possible through apprenticeship,

    - Mainly out of economic necessity, American physicians began opening medical schools

Notes

**Medical Services
In Preindustrial America**

- Medical Practice

    – Medicine was a trade without today's prestige

    – It did not require a rigorous course of study, clinical practice, residency training, board exams, or licensing

    – Anyone, trained or untrained, could practice as a physician.

**Medical Services
In Preindustrial America**

- Medical Practice

    – The clergy often combined medical services and religious duties.

    – Many physicians had a second occupation because income from medical practice alone was inadequate to support a family.

**Medical Services
In Preindustrial America**

- Medical Institutions

    – The predecessor of today's hospitals and nursing homes in the United States was
        - the almshouse (poor house).

    – Almshouses existed in almost all cities of moderate size and were run by the local government.

    – The few hospitals that did exist at this time had deplorable sanitary conditions and poor ventilation.

Medical Services
in Postindustrial America

The postindustrial era was marked by

- the growth and development of a medical profession that benefited from
  - urbanization, new scientific discoveries, and reforms in medical education.

- America's system for delivering health care took shape during this period.

Medical Services
in Postindustrial America

- Medicine became entrenched as
  - Physicians became a cohesive profession, opted for specialization and gained power and prestige.

- The hospital emerged as a repository for high-tech facilities and equipment.

- Private and public health insurance took roots.
  - Look at Exhibit 3.3, page 52

Medical Services
in Postindustrial America

- Educational Reform

- Medical Profession

- American Medical Association

- Development of Hospitals

Medical Services
in Postindustrial America

Education Reform:

- Advances in medical science necessitated the reform of medical education
  - around 1870 medical schools began affiliating with universities
  - Harvard revolutionized medical education
    - The academic year went from 4 to 9 months
    - Medical instruction went from two to three years
    - Labs and clinical courses such as chemistry, physiology, anatomy and pathology were added

Medical Services
in Postindustrial America

Education Reform:

- Johns Hopkins University opened in 1893 and required that medical education become a
  - Graduate training program
    - requiring a college degree as an entrance requirement

- The American Medical Association (AMA)
  - Pushed for state laws requiring graduation from a medical school accredited by the AMA as a basis for licensure to practice medicine

Medical Services in Postindustrial America

- Medical Profession

  - Urbanization led to the concentration of medical practice in cities and towns

    - office-based practice began to replace house calls

Medical Services in Postindustrial America

- Medical Profession

  - Medicine became driven by science and technology,
    - lay people could no longer deliver legitimate medical care

  - Advances in
    - bacteriology, antiseptic surgery, anesthesia, immunology and diagnostic techniques with new drugs helped make medical practice a legitimate profession
      - Look at Exhibit 3.4, page 54

Medical Services in Postindustrial America

- American Medical Association

  - helped galvanize the profession and protected the interest of physicians
  - The concerted activities of the collective physicians is referred to as
    - "organized medicine":
      - it distinguishes them from the uncoordinated actions of individual physicians
      - The AMA gained strength when it organized its members into county and state medical societies
      - The AMA supported states in establishing medical licensing laws

Medical Services in Postindustrial America

- American Medical Association

  - Employment of physicians by hospitals and insurance companies was frowned on.

  - AMA encouraged independence from corporate control and promoted private entrepreneurship

Notes

Medical Services in Postindustrial America

- Development of Hospitals

  - The growth of hospitals came to symbolize the institutionalization of health care

  - Advancements in medical science created the need to

    - centralize expensive facilities and equipment in an institution,
      - advanced medical devices; the training of health care personnel; and facilities for surgical procedures, advanced diagnostics, and medical treatment became centered in the hospital

History of Health Insurance

- Also called "voluntary health insurance"

- The expansion of health insurance and rising costs
  - prompted Congress to create publicly financed Medicare and Medicaid programs for the most vulnerable populations

History of Health Insurance

- Workers' Compensation

- Rise of Private Health Insurance
  - First Hospital Plan and the Birth of Blue Cross
  - First Physician Plan and the Birth of Blue Shield
  - Employer-based Health Insurance

- Failure of National Health Care Proposals

- Creation of Medicaid and Medicare

History of Health Insurance

Workers' Compensation

- was the first broad-coverage health insurance in the United States

- was originally designed to make cash payments to workers for wages lost because of job-related injuries and disease.

- later became compensation for medical expenses, and death benefits for survivors were added.

- was a trial for a government-sponsored health insurance, but
  - private health insurance has prevented a national health care program

History of Health Insurance

- Rise of Private Health Insurance

  - Private insurance began as
    - a form of disability coverage that provided income during temporary disability due to bodily injury or illness

  - During the 1900's
    - medical treatments and hospital care advanced, but medical care also became more expensive
      - people could not predict their future needs for medical care or its cost.

History of Health Insurance

- Rise of Private Health Insurance
  - Hospital Plan and Birth of Blue Cross
    - The Great Depression made hospitals economically unstable
      - and individuals faced the loss of income from illness and the debt of high health care costs
    - In 1929, Justin Kimball began
      - a hospital insurance plan for teachers at Baylor University Hospital in Dallas, Texas
        - it became the model for Blue Cross plans around the country
    - The American Hospital Association (AHA) supported group hospital plans and coordinated them into a Blue Cross network

Notes

History of Health Insurance

- First Physician Plan and the Birth of Blue Shield

  - In 1939, the California Medical Association started the first Blue Shield plan
    - it was designed to pay physician fees

  - By 1974, Blue Cross and Blue Shield merged

  - Today they are a joint corporation, and are in almost every state

History of Health Insurance

- Rise of Private Health Insurance
  - Employer-based Health Insurance

    - During World War II, employees accepted employer-paid health insurance to compensate for the loss of raises

    - Congress made employer-provided health coverage nontaxable
      - this was equivalent to getting more salary without having to pay taxes

    - Employment-based health insurance became the vehicle for the delivery of health care

History of Health Insurance

- Failure of National Health Care Proposals
  - The entry of the United States into World War I in 1917 was a political blow to the national health care movement
    - as anti-German feelings were aroused and the US government denounced German social insurance.
    - Opponents of national health care called it inconsistent with American values.

  - The AMA has always been opposed because
    - it is perceived as a threat to private practice

  - Often stigmatized as government interference or socialized medicine

History of Health Insurance

- Failure of National Health Care Proposals

  - The most recent failure was initiated by the Clinton Administration

    - Polls confirmed that health care reform was a major issue

    - Americans endorse a tax-supported plan to help the needy, but
      - They are unwilling to pay higher taxes

History of Health Insurance

- Creation of Medicaid and Medicare

  - Before 1965, private health insurance was the only widely available source of payment for health care,

    - and it was available primarily to middle-class working people and their families.

    - A three-part program was adopted
      - Medicare Parts A and B, and Medicaid

History of Health Insurance

- Creation of Medicaid and Medicare

- Medicare Part A
  - was designed to use Social Security funds to finance hospital bills

- Medicare Part B
  - was designed to cover physicians' bills
    - through government-subsidized insurance
      - the elderly would pay part of the premiums.

Notes

Notes

History of Health Insurance

- Creation of Medicaid and Medicare

  - Although adopted together, Medicare and Medicaid reflected sharply different traditions.

  - Medicare was upheld by broad grassroots support and, being attached to Social Security, had no class distinction.

History of Health Insurance

- Creation of Medicaid and Medicare
  - Medicaid benefits vary from state to state
    - It is means-tested
      - Confines eligibility to those below an income level

  - Medicare has uniform national standards for eligibility and benefits
    - It covers anyone over the age of 65

      - Look at Table 3.1, page 62 for a comparison of the two programs

History of Health Insurance

- Creation of Medicaid and Medicare

- The Medicare and Medicaid programs are financed by the government, but

  - enrollees receive health care services mostly from private hospitals, physicians, and other providers.

History of Health Insurance

- ● Creation of Medicaid and Medicare

- ● Government uses many regulations to govern
  - – the delivery of services and how much providers should be paid

- ● Health care delivery systems are
  - – subject to annual scrutiny by public health agencies delegated to them by the federal and state governments.

Year 1970 into the 21st Century

- ● The federal government bore the financial brunt with the creation of Medicare and Medicaid
  - – Look at Table 3.2, page 63

- ● For the federal government,
  - – Health care expenses increased at an annual rate of 30%
    - ● Compared to other expenses at a rise of only 11.3%
      - – Look at Figure 3.1, page 65
- ● To curb inflation, President Richard Nixon implemented the Economic Stabilization Program in 1971.

Year 1970 into the 21st Century

- ● Despite escalating cost,

  - – the original Medicare program was expanded in 1973 to include the disabled receiving Social Security cash benefits.

- ● In 1978, the program was extended to people with end-stage kidney disease.

Notes

_____

_____

_____

_____

_____

_____

_____

_____

_____

_____

_____

_____

_____

_____

_____

_____

_____

_____

_____

_____

_____

_____

_____

_____

_____

_____

_____

_____

_____

_____

_____

_____

_____

_____

_____

_____

_____

_____

_____

_____

_____

Year 1970 into the 21st Century

- During the 1990's,
  - managed care was largely credited with containing double-digit inflation in health care costs.

- The 1990's were marked by
  - mergers and acquisitions between hospitals, and between hospitals and physician clinics.

- The United States now has
  - an expanding market of self-care products and alternative therapies.

- This consumer-driven phenomenon has not gone unnoticed by the traditional medical establishment

---

Year 1970 into the 21st Century

- New diseases continue to present fresh challenges.

- The medical research community diligently continues its efforts to find cures for new and old health problems.

- The AIDS pandemic presents major challenges around the globe.

Year 1970 into the 21st Century

- Bioterrorism
  - is the latest threat gripping the nation since September 11, 2001.

- Resources are deployed to counteract the possibility of clandestine warfare with deadly agents such as
  - smallpox, a disease eradicated from the planet in 1977

Year 1970 into the 21st Century

- With the aging population and longer life expectancies,
  - the number of people with chronic conditions will rise dramatically.

- By 2030,
  - over 170 million Americans are projected to have a chronic condition.

Year 1970 into the 21st Century

- The indiscriminate growth and use of medical technologies has fueled health care costs.

- Future emphasis will be on the use of technologies that lead to greater efficiency in the delivery of health care.

Year 1970 into the 21st Century

- The Internet
  - is empowering patients

- Access to expert information is no longer strictly confined to the physician's domain.

Notes

Year 1970 into the 21st Century

- The influx of immigrants is creating new challenges

- Their disproportionate representation among the uninsured receives greater attention.

Year 1970 into the 21st Century

- Politics sometimes affects health care delivery as seen in the passage of the

  - Medicare Prescription Drug Improvement and Modernization Act of 2003, signed into law by President George W. Bush.

Year 1970 into the 21st Century

- Medical malpractice awards and unaffordable medical insurance costs are driving some physicians out of medical practice

- Physicians have lost much autonomy with the domain of major hospital-based systems

- Many corporate alliances are still being formed

Conclusion

● In just over 100 years,

   – health care has come from a primitive craft to a technology-driven service where health care is the largest industry in the United States

   – Health care delivery has been transformed by
- Technological advances
- Emergence of new diseases
- Threat of bioterrorism
- The rise of chronic disease in the growing elderly population
- Organizational transformations

Conclusion

● The health care industry has grown regardless of the state of the general economy

● The debate over national health care coverage will emerge on occasion, but how Americans will pay for it will be the challenge

Notes

Chapter 4: Health Care Providers and Professionals

Notes

Chapter 4

Health Care
Providers
and
Professionals

Introduction

The US health care industry is the largest and most powerful employer in the nation

- It employs more than 3% of the total labor force in the United States

- The growth of health care services is closely linked to the demand for health services professionals

---

Physicians

- All states require physicians to be licensed to practice.

- The licensure requirements include:
  - graduation from an accredited medical school that
    - awards a Doctor of Medicine (MD) or Doctor of Osteopathic Medicine (DO)
  - successful completion of a licensing examination governed by either the National Board of Medical Examiners, or the National Board of Osteopathic Medical Examiners
  - completion of a supervised internship/residency program

Similarities and Differences between MDs and DOs

- Both MDs and DOs use
  - Traditionally-accepted methods of treatment,
    - including drugs and surgery

  - Osteopathic medicine, practiced by DOs, emphasizes the musculoskeletal system, such as correction of joint tissues

Similarities and Differences between MDs and DOs

- MDs

  - Are trained in allopathic medicine, which views medical treatment as

    - active intervention to produce a counteracting reaction in an attempt to neutralize the effects of disease

Generalists and Specialists

Physicians trained in

- family medicine/general practice,
- general internal medicine
- and general pediatrics

  - are considered primary care physicians or generalists

Generalists and Specialists

Specialists must seek certification in an area of medical specialization

- which commonly requires additional years of advanced residency training, followed by several years of practice in the specialty

Work Settings and Practice Patterns

- Physicians practice in a variety of settings and arrangements.

- Some work in hospitals as medical residents or staff physicians

- Others work in the public sector, in federal government agencies, public health clinics, etc.

Dentists

- The major role of dentists is to
  - diagnose and treat problems related to teeth, gums, and tissues of the mouth

- All dentists must be licensed to practice

- Some states require dentists to obtain a specialty license before practicing as a specialist in that state.

Pharmacists

The role of pharmacists has expanded from

– the preparation and dispensing of prescriptions to include:

- drug product education

- serving as experts on specific drugs, drug interaction, and generic drug substitution

Other Doctoral – Level Health Professionals

- <u>Psychologists</u> provide patients with
  – mental health care

- <u>Podiatrists</u> treat patients with
  – disease or deformities of the feet, including surgical operations

  – medications and corrective devices

  – physiotherapy

Other Doctoral – Level Health Professionals

Chiropractors

– Provide treatment to patients through:

- chiropractic manipulation

- physiotherapy

- dietary counseling.

Nurses

- Nurses are
  - the major caregivers of sick and injured patients
    - addressing their physical, mental, and emotional needs.

- All states require nurses to be licensed to practice

- Nurses work in a variety of settings:
  - hospitals
  - nursing homes
  - private practice
  - ambulatory care centers
  - community
  - migrant health centers, etc.

Advanced – Practice Nurses (APN)

There are four areas of specialization for APNs:

- clinical nurse specialists (CNS),

- certified registered nurse anesthetists (CRNAs),

- nurse practitioners (NPs),

- certified nurse-midwives (CNMs)

Non-Physician Practitioners (NPP)

- NPPs
  - receive less advance training than physicians
    - but more training than registered nurses (RN).

- They do not:
  - engage in the entire range of primary care, or
  - deal with cases requiring the expertise of a physician

Value of NPP Services

- Studies have
  - confirmed the efficacy of NPPs as health care providers.
  - demonstrated that NPPs can provide
    - both high-quality and cost-effective medical care because

- NPPs
  - show greater personal interest in patients, and
  - cost less

Value of NPP Services

Issues that need to be resolved before NPPs can be used to their full potential are:

- legal restrictions on practice,

- reimbursement policies, and

- relationships with physicians

Allied Health Professionals

Technicians and Assistants

- receive less than two years of post-secondary education and are trained to perform procedures

- require supervision from therapists or technologists to
  - ensure that care plan evaluation occurs as part of treatment

Allied Health Professionals

- Technologists and Therapists
  - learn how to:
    - evaluate patients,
    - diagnose problems, and
    - develop treatment plans

- Education for the technologist or therapist includes:
  - skill development in teaching procedural skills to technicians

Health Service Administrators

Health services administrators are

- employed at the top, middle, and entry levels of various types of organizations that deliver health services

- are responsible for the
  - operational, clinical, and financial outcomes of the entire organization.

Health Service Administrators

Health Service Administrators

- are taught at the bachelor's and master's level
  - in a variety of settings, and
  - the programs lead to several different degrees

- constitute the largest portion of the labor force

Notes

Chapter 5: Technology and Its Effects

Notes

Chapter 5

Technology
and Its Effects

Introduction

- Medical technology has brought numerous benefits to modern civilization

- Technology has also allowed critically ill patients to be put on life support with limited decision-making abilities and little hope of full recovery

Introduction

Technology prolongs life

    – elderly consume more health care than younger people

What is Medical Technology?

- The practical application of the scientific body of knowledge produced by biomedical research

What is Medical Technology

- Advances in organic chemistry made it possible to
  - identify and extract the active ingredients found in natural plants to
    - produce drugs and anesthetics

- Medical technology includes:
  - sophisticated machines
  - pharmaceuticals
  - biological

Information Technology

Computerized information systems have become indispensable for:

- managing patient care management

- quality improvement,

- cost containment, and

- other aspects of operating health care organizations

The Internet

- Has already begun to revolutionize aspects of health care delivery,
  - its use will continue to grow

- By accessing information from the Internet,
  - patients are more active participants in their own health care

Patient Privacy

One critical issue associated with the wide use of information technology is:

  - the confidentiality of patient information

Patient Privacy

The law made it illegal to gain access to

  - personal medical information for reasons other than health care delivery, operations, and reimbursement

Use of Medical Technology

- High-tech procedures are

  - more readily-available in the United States than they are in most other countries

- Little is done to limit the expansion of new medical technology

Use of Medical Technology

- To control medical cost, almost all other nations have tried to limit, mainly through central planning, the

  - distribution and utilization of high-tech procedures

- Implementing these measures would be contrary to the fundamental beliefs and values of Americans

Cultural Beliefs and Values

- American beliefs and values have been instrumental in determining the nature of health care delivery in the United States

- Capitalism and lack of government intervention promotes innovation

Cultural Beliefs and Values

The technological imperative

– the desire to:

- have state-of-the-art technology available and

- use it despite its cost

Medical Training and Practice

What predominates in the medical culture of the United States is:

– emphasis on specialty care over primary care and preventive services

Medical Training and Practice

An oversupply of specialists has led to the development and use of new technology

– primary care physicians use less technology than specialists

Payment for Services

Evidence from several countries suggest that:

– fixed provider payments and strong limits on payments to hospitals curtail the incentive to use high-tech procedures

Competition

- Specialization has been used as an enticement to attract insured patients

  – Such practices have resulted in duplication of services

- Equipment has further contributed to medical specialization

Role of the Government in Technology Diffusion

- The development and dissemination of technology is called *technology diffusion*

  - It addresses when technology will be made available for use, and where it can be accessed

Role of the Government in Technology Diffusion

Technology diffusion has been accompanied by issues of:

- cost

- safety

- benefit

- risk

Regulation of Drugs and Devices

The Food and Drug Administration (FDA) is

- an agency of the US Department of Health and Human Services (DHHS)

- the FDA is responsible for
  - ensuring that drugs and medical devices are safe and effective for their intended use

Impact of Medical Technology

- The effects of advanced scientific knowledge and medical technology have been far-reaching and pervasive

- The effects often overlap
  - it is difficult to pinpoint the impact of technology on the delivery of health care

Notes

Notes

Impact on Quality of Care

Quality is

- enhanced only when new procedures can
  - prevent or delay the onset of serious disease
  - provide a better diagnosis
  - make faster and more complete cures possible
  - increase safety of medical treatment
  - minimize undesirable side effects
  - promote faster recoveries from surgery
  - increase life expectancy
  - improve quality of life

Impact on Quality of Life

- Quality of life indicates
  - a patient's overall satisfaction with life during and after medical treatment

- Major technological advances have furnished the clinical ability to help patients cope with:
  - diabetes
  - heart disease
  - end-stage renal disease
  - HIV-AIDS

Impact on Quality of Life

Procedures such as coronary artery bypass graft (an open surgical procedure to correct blockage of coronary arteries) have made it possible for people with serious heart disease to return to normal activity a few weeks after surgery

Impact on Health Care Costs

The measurement of the impact of technology on health care costs is imprecise but technology proliferation has unquestionably contributed to rising health care expenditures

Impact on Health Care Costs

In other industries
- new technology often reduces the labor force and production costs
  - in health care, the addition of new technology usually increases both labor and capital costs
    - an inverse relationship

Impact on Access

Geographic access can be improved

- with new mobile equipment or communication technologies that allow remote access to centralized equipment and specialized personnel

Notes

Impact on Bioethics

- gene mapping of humans,
- genetic cloning,
- stem cell research,
- other areas of growing interest

  – may hold potential benefits

  – but also represent serious ethical dilemmas

Assessment of Medical Technology

Technology assessment refers to:
- the evaluation of medical technology to determine:
  - its safety,
  - effectiveness,
  - feasibility and indication for use, and
  - cost-effectiveness

- The objective of technology assessment is to:
  - establish the appropriateness of medical technology for widespread use

Efficacy

- Efficacy is:
  - the health benefit to be derived from technology

  - or how effective technology is in diagnosing or treating a condition

- If a product or service actually produces some health benefits,
  - it can be considered efficacious of effective

Safety

- Safety considerations are designed to:
  - protect patients against unnecessary harm from the use of technology

- After safety has been experimentally determined,
  - outcomes from the wider use of technology are monitored over time to identify any problems

Cost-Effectiveness

- Cost-effectiveness or cost-efficiency
  - is beyond the determination of efficacy and safety

- It is cost-effective when
  - technology is introduced, and the benefits exceed the cost

Benefits of Technology Assessment

Delivering Value

- The concept of value-improved benefits at lower cost is

  - important to those who finance health care organizations

- Value is enhanced as costs are reduced

Benefits of Technology Assessment

Cost Containment

    – technology seems to be the culprit for cost escalations

        • However, constraining technology dissemination would be a misdirected strategy

Benefits of Technology Assessment

-Standardized Practice Protocols

    – Medical practice guideline are protocols to assist practitioners in delivering appropriate health care for specific clinical circumstances
    – Practice guidelines result from
        • an evaluation of medical procedures
        • appropriateness
        • safety
        • the integration of these assessments into clinical practice

Notes

_____
_____
_____
_____
_____
_____
_____
_____
_____
_____
_____
_____
_____
_____
_____
_____
_____
_____
_____
_____
_____
_____
_____
_____
_____
_____
_____
_____
_____
_____
_____
_____
_____
_____

Chapter 6

Financing and Reimbursement Methods

Introduction

- **Financing is:**

  - any mechanism that gives people the ability to pay for health care services.

- **In most cases, financing is necessary to have access to health care**

Introduction

The primary sources of finance in the U.S. that allow for access to health care are through:

- the purchase of health insurance or eligibility in a public insurance program such as Medicare or Medicaid,

- uncompensated or charity care
  - usually free clinics and hospital emergency rooms

Introduction

Complexity of financing:

- a primary characteristic of health care delivery in U.S.
- many payers
- many plans
- many programs
- many payment options

- Refer to Figure 6-1

Introduction

- **The primary financiers of health care in the United States are:**
  - employers and the government

- **From an economic perspective, Americans already finance their own health care, either through:**
  - employment or taxes

Introduction

U.S. has a voluntary system
- employers not mandated to offer insurance
- government covers certain groups

Role and Scope of Health Care Financing

- Health insurance
  - primary mechanism to obtain health care
  - regarded as key to health care finance

- Finance determines who has access to health care

- Demand is related to finance

- Insurance lowers out-of-pocket payments, hence patients consume more

The Insurance Function

- Insurance
  - protects against risk

- Risk
  - the possibility of substantial financial loss from some event, where
    - probability of occurrence is small

The Insurance Function

- Insured
  - an individual protected by insurance

- Insurer
  - an insurance agency that assumes the risk

- Underwriting
  - evaluates, selects/rejects, classifies, and rates risk

Notes

Notes

Health Insurance Concepts

- **Beneficiary**
  - "the insured"
  - covered under a health insurance plan

- **Premiums**
  - amount charged by insurer to be insured against risk
  - in a job-based plan, employer and employees pay into rate

The Insurance Function

Four Principles of Insurance:

1) Risk is unpredictable

2) Risk can be predictable with some accuracy in a large group

3) Insurance can shift risk from the individual to the group through pooling resources

4) Losses are shared by all members

Health Insurance Concepts

Cost Sharing

- Insurance requires some type of *cost sharing*

- The insured assumes at least part of the risk

- The purpose of cost sharing is to reduce misuse of insurance benefits.

Health Insurance Concepts

Cost Sharing

– There are three main types of cost sharing in private health insurance:

  • premium cost sharing,

  • deductibles, and

  • copayments

Health Insurance Concepts

Cost Sharing

– <u>Deductibles</u>
  • the amount the insured pays first before benefits are paid by the plan

  • paid out-of-pocket each time health services are received

– <u>Copayment</u>
  • money paid out-of-pocket each time health services are received

  • paid after the deductible has been met

Health Insurance Concepts

Cost Sharing

– <u>Coinsurance</u>
  • 80/20 ratio of cost sharing between insurance plan and the insured

– <u>Stop-loss provision</u>
  • maximum out-of-pocket liability an insurance agency would insure in a given year

Notes

Notes

Health Insurance Concepts

Service Plans

- provide services to the insured

- pay the hospital and physician directly except for:
  - deductibles and copayments

Types of Private Insurance

Group insurance

- offered through an employer, a union, or professional organization

- anticipates large numbers of people in a group will buy insurance through a sponsor

- cost and risk are distributed equally among the insured

Types of Private Insurance

Self-insurance

- big employers' workforces are large and diversified enough that:
  - they can predict their own medical experience

- large employers:
  - assume risk
  - don't have to pay insurers a dividend

Types of Private Insurance

Self-insurance

– <u>Reinsurance</u>

  • Employers can protect themselves against the potential risk of high losses

    – Purchased from a private insurance company

– Many employers find managed care to be more economical

  • consequently, the number of self-insured plans declined during the 1990s.

Types of Private Insurance

Individual Private Health Insurance

  – an important source of coverage for many Americans

  – covers 5.1% of the non-elderly population

    • 12 million people

Types of Private Insurance

Managed Care Plans

• **Managed Care Organizations (MCO) consist of:**

  – Health Maintenance Organizations (HMO)

  – Preferred Provider Organizations (PPO)

    • They assume the risk in exchange for an insurance premium

    • They provide a broad range of service, emphasizing primary care and prevention

Notes

Notes

Public Financing

Government financing

- accounted for 45.4% of total U.S. health care expenditures
  - Look at Figure 6-2

- New prescription drug coverage to Medicare will
  - further shift the burden of national health care spending to taxpayers

Public Financing

- **Public financing supports *categorical programs*,**
  - each designed to benefit a certain category of people who
    - meet the eligibility criteria to become beneficiaries

- **Medicare and Medicaid are**
  - categorical programs and were created under
    - the Social Security Amendments (1965)

Public Financing

Medicare

- Title XVIII of Social Security Act

- an entitlement program
  - people contribute through taxes and are entitled regardless of income and assets

- a federal program
  - administered by the Centers for Medicare and Medicaid Services (CMS), an agency under the U.S. Department of Health and Human Services (DHHS).

Public Financing

Medicare

– finances medical care for:

1) those 65 years old or older

2) disabled people who are entitled to Social Security benefits

3) those with end-stage renal disease

Public Financing

Medicare

- has a dual structure
  - comprising two separate insurance programs that are distinct regarding
    - benefits,
    - coverage,
    - financing, and
    - administration.

- These two programs are referred to as:
  - Part A and
  - Part B.

Public Financing

Medicare

– Hospital insurance (Part A)

- Is financed by payroll taxes collected by Social Security

- Has mandatory taxes that are:
  - paid by all working individuals, including those who are self-employed
  - all earnings are subject to the Medicare tax

- Taxes finance the hospital insurance Trust Fund

Public Financing

Medicare

– Hospital insurance (Part A)

• Covers:

– inpatient services,

– short-term convalescence and rehabilitation in a skilled nursing facility (SNF),

– home health, and

– hospice

– Look at Figure 6-3

Public Financing

Medicare

– Hospital insurance (Part A)

• For hospital and nursing home stay,

– the timing of benefits is determined by a *benefit period*.

» It begins on the day a beneficiary is hospitalized.

» It ends when the beneficiary has not been in a hospital or a skilled nursing facility for 60 consecutive days.

» If after 60 days the beneficiary is hospitalized again, a new benefit period begins.

– The number of benefit periods a beneficiary can have over his or her lifetime is unlimited

---

Public Financing

Medicare

• Benefits under Part A for acute care, post-acute skilled nursing care, home health and hospice

1. All covered hospital services are paid for the first 60 days in a benefit period,

– after a deductible ($876 in 2004) has been paid

2. Medicare pays for up to 100 days of care in a Medicare-certified SNF

– subsequent to inpatient hospitalization for at least three consecutive days, not including the day of discharge

Notes

Public Financing

Medicare

3. Medicare pays for home health care when a person is:
   - homebound and requires intermittent or part-time skilled nursing care or rehabilitation care

4. For the terminally ill,
   - Medicare pays for care provided by a Medicare-certified hospice program

Public Financing

Medicare
  - Supplementary Medical Insurance (SMI)
    - (Part B or Medigap policies)
      - Covers:
        » physician services,
        » hospital outpatient services (surgery),
        » diagnostic tests,
        » radiology,
        » emergency department,
        » rehab,
        » ambulance,
        » dialysis,
        » radiation,
        » durable medical equipment

Public Financing

Medicare

- Medigaps, SMI, or Part B
  - covers all or a portion of Medicare deductibles and copayments,
  - may pay for services not covered by Medicare
  - are voluntary programs paid partly by general tax revenue and a premium
    - In 2001, 94% of all Medicare enrollees had a supplement

Public Financing

Medicare

- **Noncovered Services**

  – **Parts A and B offer comprehensive care**

    - vision,
    - eyeglasses,
    - dentures,
    - hearing aids,
    - preventative services,
    - routine physicals

Public Financing

Medicare

  – **Prescription drug benefits:**

    - **On December 8, 2003, President George W. Bush signed the**

      – **Medicare Prescription Drug, Improvement and Modernization Act (MMA) of 2003,**

        » **It expanded Medicare for the first time**

        » **Medicare beneficiaries can voluntarily enroll in the program.**

Public Financing

Medicare

  – **Prescription drug benefits:**

    - **The program will take effect in two stages:**

    1. **Medicare contracts with private companies to offer drug discount cards**

      - **allows beneficiaries to save 10% to 25%**

Public Financing

Medicare

- Prescription drug benefits:

2. Will begin in 2006 with:

- • voluntary enrollment
- • a monthly premium of $35
- • an annual deductible of $250
- • benefits paid according to three layers of personal out-of-pocket spending

---

Public Financing

Medicare

- Prescription drug benefits:
  - • benefits paid on three layers of personal out-of-pocket spending by each beneficiary

Spending	Medicare Coverage
1) $250 to $2,250	75% of costs
2) $2,250 to $3,600	No coverage
3) $3,600 +	95% of costs

- designed to help at a basic threshold and then those who have excessive needs

---

Public Financing

Medicare+Choice

- called "Medicare Advantage"

- took effect on January 1, 1998

- mandated by the Balanced Budget Act (BBA) of 1997

Public Financing

Medicare+Choice

- enrollees can enroll in one of the three programs:
  1. **Medicare Managed Care Plans**
     - beneficiaries to seek care only from physicians and hospitals participating in an HMO network
  2. **Medicare Private Fee-for-Service Plans**
     - beneficiaries seek care from a physician or hospital that accepts the plan's payment
  3. **Medicare Preferred Provider Organization (PPO)**
     - beneficiaries seek care from in-network providers, or
     - go outside the network at a higher personal out-of-pocket expense

Public Financing

Medicaid

- Title XIX of Social Security Act

- finances health care for the indigent, but not all poor

- each state establishes its own eligibility according to:
  - income and resources such as bank accounts and assets

- each state administers its own Medicaid program

Public Financing

Medicaid

- states define "medically needy" categories based on income and assets
  » Look at Figure 6-4

- for a state to receive federal matching funds,
  - federal law mandates every state provide basic health services
    - Look at Table 6-1

Public financing

Medicaid

- A means-tested program
  - Qualify based on assets and income being below state threshold

- Jointly financed by federal and state government
  - Federal government matches states based on per capita income

Programs Under Balanced Budget Act 1997

State Children's Health Insurance Program (SCHIP)

- Title XXI of Social Security Act

- additional funds to states to expand Medicaid for children under 19 years

- available to families with incomes up to:
  - 200% of federal poverty level or
  - about $37,700 for a family of four in 2004

Military Health Services System (MHSS)

U.S. Department of Defense

- health care for those on active duty and retirees, and their dependents and survivors

- 8.3 million are eligible

- staffed mostly by military personnel for active-duty members

- dependents and retirees can receive health care under TriCare

Military Health Services System

U.S. Department of Defense
- Tricare health plan options:
  1) TriCare Prime
     - functions like an HMO with a Primary Care Manager
     - the most cost-efficient
  2) TriCare Extra
     - a preferred provider option
     - receive medical care from participating civilian network providers at a discount
     - has an expanded network of providers
  3) TriCare Standard
     - fee-for-service
     - services are provided by civilians
     - greatest choice of physicians but at a higher cost

Veterans Health Administration (VHA)

The health services branch of the Veteran Administration

- An Executive Department of the U.S. government

- one of the largest health service network in U.S.
  - 172 hospitals
  - 860 outpatient clinics
  - 137 nursing homes

Veterans Health Administration (VHA)

- Organized into 22 geographically distributed VISNs
  - Veterans Integrated Service Networks (VISNs)
    - Each VISN receives an allotment of federal funds and is responsible for equitable distribution of funds among hospitals and providers
- Care is given on a priority basis to:
  - veterans with a service-connected illness or disability

REIMBURSEMENT METHODS

- **Third-party payers**
  - insurance companies, managed care organizations, BlueCross BlueShield, government

- **Reimbursement**
  - payment made by third-party payers to the providers of services

REIMBURSEMENT METHODS

Fee-for-Service
- Charges were set by providers
- Each service is billed separately (i.e. examination, x-ray, urinalysis)
- Insurers later limited reimbursement to:
  - a "usual, customary, and reasonable" (UCR) amount
    - determined by each payer
  - providers would balance bill,
    - patients pay the difference between the actual charges and the payments received from insurers
- Main drawback
  - providers induce demand

REIMBURSEMENT METHODS

Package pricing (bundled pricing)

- number of related services in one price

- reduces provider-induced demand because fees are inclusive of all bundle services
  - (i.e., optometry includes exam, frames, and lenses)

Notes

Notes

REIMBURSEMENT METHODS

Resource-Based Relative Value Scale (RBRVS)

- Under the Omnibus Budget Reconciliation Act of 1989
  - (OBRA-89)

- Medicare developed an initiative to reimburse physicians according to a "relative value" assigned to each service
  - based on time, skill, intensity
  - complex formula

REIMBURSEMENT METHODS

Resource-Based Relative Value Scale (RBRVS)

- Each year, Medicare publishes the Medicare Fee Schedule (MFS)
  - It gives the reimbursement amounts for each of the services and procedures under
    - a CPT (current procedural terminology) code
    - reimbursements are adjusted for the geographic area
- Goal: Narrow gap between incomes of specialists and generalists

REIMBURSEMENT METHODS

Managed care approaches

1. Capitation
   - Per member, per month fee to cover all needed services
   - Incentive to give only services needed
   - Minimize provider-induced demand
   - Drawback:
     - Incentive to limit services can result in underutilization of services

REIMBURSEMENT METHODS

Managed care approaches

2. Retrospective reimbursement

- rates were set after evaluating the costs retrospectively
- historical costs are used to determine the amount to be paid

REIMBURSEMENT METHODS

Managed care approaches

3. Prospective reimbursement
- uses certain preestablished criteria to determine in advance the amount of reimbursement

- Medicare has been using the prospective payment system (PPS) to reimburse inpatient hospital acute care services under Medicare Part A since 1983

REIMBURSEMENT METHODS

Managed care approaches

3. Prospective reimbursement

- Four main prospective reimbursement methods:
  - Diagnosis Related Groups (DRG)
  - Ambulatory Payment Classifications (APC)
  - Resources Utilization Groups (RUG)
  - Home Health Resources Group (HHRG)

REIMBURSEMENT METHODS

Diagnosis-Related Groups (DRGs)

– for hospital inpatients, reimbursement:
  - has forced hospitals to control costs, keeping actual costs below the fixed reimbursement amount, as they get to keep the difference as profit

– approximately 500 DRGs

– prospectively set a bundled price
  - according to the admitting diagnosis

REIMBURSEMENT METHODS

Ambulatory Payment Classification (APC)

– prospective payment method implemented in August, 2000

– associated with Medicare's Outpatient Prospective Payment System (OPPS)

– for services provided by hospital outpatient departments

– 300 procedure groups

– reimbursement rates are associated with each APC group

– a bundled rate to include:
  - anesthesia, drugs, supplies, recovery

REIMBURSEMENT METHODS

Resource Utilization Groups (RUG)

– are a case-mix method to reimburse Skilled Nursing Facilities (SNF)
  - Case mix
    – overall acuity level in a facility

– used for determining a SNF's overall intensity of health conditions requiring medical and nursing intervention

– each patient is classified into one of 44 RUGs

– the case mix determines a fixed per-diem
  - the higher the case mix score, the higher the reimbursement

REIMBURSEMENT METHODS

Home Health Resource Groups (HHRG)

- implemented October, 2000

- pay a fixed, pre-determined rate
  - for each 60-day episode of care, regardless of services given

- services are bundled under one payment on a per-patient basis

- 80 distinct groups to indicate severity of a patient's condition

National Health Expenditures

- An estimate of the amount spent for all health services, supplies, health-related research and construction activities in the United States during a calendar year:

  - In 2001, $1.425 trillion spent on national health care expenditures in U.S.

National Health Expenditures

To compare the total expenditures on health to the total economic consumption, use:

- Gross Domestic Product (GDP)
  - It measures the total value of goods and services produced and consumed.
  - In 2001, the GDP was $10.082 trillion.
    - Hence, 14.1% of the total economic output in 2001 was consumed by health care
    - $5,035 per capita spending on average
    - Look at Table 6-2

National Health Expenditures

In 2001,

- – 87% of total national health expenses were spent on:
  - • personal health (i.e., hospital care, physician services, dental care, other professional services, nursing home care, home health care, prescription drugs, medical supplies, durable medical equipment, vision care)
- – Remaining 13% was spent on:
  - • Public Health services, research, construction, administrative services

National Health Expenditures

Cost inflation in health care is evaluated by

- – comparing it to the growth of GDP and also to the consumer price index (CPI)

  - • CPI measures inflation in the general economy

  - • health care cost inflation has exceeded the growth in GDP and CPI

    – Look at Table 6-3

Conclusion

Financing plays a critical function in health care delivery

- – For consumers, it pays for insurance coverage, which enables them to obtain health care services.

- – For providers, it reimburses them for the services they provide.

Conclusion

- Methods of reimbursement changed from retrospective to prospective

- Prospective payment and capitation used by HMOs contain incentives for the delivery of cost-effective health care

Conclusion

Financing is shared between private and public sources

- government incurs over 45% of all health care expenditures in the United States
  - a quasi-national health care system
  - public expenditure is expected to grow with
    - recent expansion of Medicare and
    - a growing elderly population

Notes

Chapter 7

Outpatient Services
and Primary Care

Outpatient and Primary Care Services
Introduction

- Hospitals were major players in outpatient services as the range of services expanded
- Health care delivery has increasingly shifted outside of expensive acute care hospitals
- Hospital labs and diagnostic services are better equipped
- Solo practices consolidated to cope
- Government agencies have sponsored limited outpatient services to meet the needs of underserved populations

---

What is Outpatient Care?

- Outpatient and Ambulatory care used interchangeably

- "Outpatient" is more comprehensive

- Outpatient services do not require overnight inpatient stay

What is Outpatient Care?

Ambulatory care constitutes:

■diagnostic and therapeutic services and treatments

provided to the "walking" (ambulatory) patient

■The term can be used synonymously with "community medicine"

■the geographic location of ambulatory services is intended for the purpose of serving the surrounding community, providing convenience and easy accessibility.

What is Outpatient Care?

■ Ambulatory Care:
■ Care rendered to patients who come to the:
■physician's office,
■clinics
■outpatient surgery

■ Mobile diagnostic units and home health
■ take services to patients

What is Outpatient Care?

■There has been extraordinary growth in the:

■volume of outpatient services and

■emergence of new types of settings

■type and ownership of non–hospital-based facilities offering ambulatory care

Scope of Outpatient Services

- Hospital inpatient services continues to decline

- Executives see Ambulatory Care as an essential, no longer a supplemental, service line

- Hospital survival can depend heavily on Ambulatory Care

- Competition from home health agencies, Ambulatory Care, urgent care, outpatient surgery

Scope of Outpatient Services

Reasons for Growth
- Changes in reimbursement
  - financial incentives to reimburse for outpatient care
  - patients favoring outpatient services
- Development of New Technology
  - less invasive procedures
    - surgical procedures less traumatic
  - shorter-acting anesthetics
  - faster recovery time

Scope of Outpatient Services

Reasons for Growth
- Utilization Controls
  - inpatient hospital stay has been strongly discouraged by various payers
  - prior authorization (pre-certification) required, minimizing length of stay
- Social factors
  - Patients have a strong preference for
    - receiving health care in home and community-based settings
    - gives people a sense of independence and control over their lives,
      - important for quality of life

Notes

Primary Care

- the conceptual foundation for ambulatory health services

Types of Outpatient Care Settings and Methods of Delivery

A myriad of:

- private practice
- hospital-based services
- free-standing facilities
- mobile medical, diagnostic, and screening services
- home health care
- hospice services
- ambulatory long-term care services
- public health services
- public and voluntary clinics
- telephone access
- alternative medicine

Types of Outpatient Care Settings and Methods of Delivery

1. Private practice
   - Office-based physicians
     - form the backbone of ambulatory care
   - It's the vast majority of primary care services
   - limited examination and testing
   - visits are short in duration
   - Solo practices merged into groups due to:
     - uncertainties of the health care delivery system,
     - competition from large health organizations,
     - high cost of establishing a new practice,
     - complexity of billings and collections
     - increased external controls over private practice

Types of Outpatient Care Settings and Methods of Delivery

2. Hospital-Based Outpatient Services

- Functions particularly in inner-city areas
  - the community's safety net, providing primary care to the indigent and uninsured

- A key source of profits for hospitals
- Five main types:
  - clinical (typically for uninsured or research)
  - surgical (same day surgery),
  - home health (post-acute care and rehabilitation),
  - women's health, and
  - traditional emergency

Types of Outpatient Care Settings and Methods of Delivery

3. Free-standing Facilities
  - Walk-in Clinics
    - Ambulatory care from basic primary to urgent care
    - Nonroutine, episodic basis
  - Urgent Care Centers
    - Accept patients without appointments
    - Wide range of routine services
    - First come, first serve basis
  - Surgi-centers
    - Freestanding, independent of hospitals
    - Full range of services for surgeries
    - Outpatient, no overnight

Types of Outpatient Care Settings and Methods of Delivery

4. Mobile Medical, Diagnostic and Screening Service

- Mobile Health Units
  - Transported to patients
    - (i.e., ambulances with Emergency Medical Technicians)

- Mobile Diagnostic Care Unit
  - Mammography
  - Magnetic Resonance Imaging

Types of Outpatient Care Settings and Methods of Delivery

5. Home Health
   - Service brought into the home
     - nursing care;
     - change dressings
     - medication monitoring;
     - bathing
     - short-term rehabilitation (PT, OT, ST)
     - homemaker services (meal prep, shopping, transportation, medical equipment, chores)
     - durable medical equipment (wheelchairs, oxygen, beds, walkers, commodes)
   - Alternative would be institutionalization
   - Maintaining people in the least restrictive environment possible

Types of Outpatient Care Settings and Methods of Delivery

6. Hospice
   - Services for the terminally ill with life expectancy of six months or less
   - Provides services that address the special needs of dying persons and their families
   - A method of care, not a location
   - Services include:
     - medical, psychological, and social services
       - provided in a holistic context and
       - access to supplies
   - Two Areas of Emphasis
     - Palliation - Pain management
     - Psychosocial and spiritual support

Types of Outpatient Care Settings and Methods of Delivery

7. Ambulatory Long-Term Care Services

   - Nursing homes
   - Case Management
     - coordination and referral
     - find most appropriate care
   - Adult Health Day Care
     - complements informal care provided at home at a center during the day

Notes

Types of Outpatient Care Settings and Methods of Delivery

8. Public Health Service

- Typically provided by
  - local health departments

- Services include:
  - well-baby care,
  - venereal disease clinics,
  - family planning services,
  - screening and treatment for tuberculosis,
  - ambulatory mental health

Types of Outpatient Care Settings and Methods of Delivery

9. Public and Voluntary Clinics
- Community Health Centers
  - authorized in the 1960s to serve the medically underserved
  - operate under the Bureau of Primary Health Care, U.S. Public Health Service, U.S. Department of Health and Human Services
- Free Clinics
  - modeled after the 19th-century dispensary
  - general ambulatory care serving the poor
  - three characteristics:
    - A. Services provided at no or a nominal charge
    - B. Not directly supported or operated by the government or the health department,
    - C. Services delivered by trained volunteers
- Other Clinics

Types of Outpatient Care Settings and Methods of Delivery

10. Telephone Access

- Telephone triage
  - Giving expert opinion and advice to the patient, especially during hours when a physician's office is usually closed
  - Nurses have:
    - access to patient records
    - guidance using protocols
    - consults with physicians

Types of Outpatient Care Settings and Methods of Delivery

11. Alternative Medicine

- "Complementary or alternative medicine"
  - not endorsed by Western medicine
  - nontraditional
  - treatments include:
    - homeopathy
    - herbal formulas
    - products as preventive and treatment agents
    - acupuncture
    - meditation
    - yoga exercises
    - biofeedback
    - spiritual guidance
    - prayer
    - chiropractic

Primary Care

- Plays a central role in a health care delivery system

- Focuses on the type or level of services:
  - prevention
  - diagnostic
  - therapeutic services
  - health education
  - counseling, and
  - minor surgery

- An approach to providing health care
  - Not a set of specific services

Primary Care

Secondary care

- usually short-term

- sporadic consultation from a specialist

- includes hospitalization

- routine surgery

- rehabilitation

Primary Care

Tertiary care

- most complex level of care
- for conditions that are uncommon
- usually institution-based
- highly specialized
- technology-driven
- rendered in large teaching hospitals
- may be long-term care
    - (i.e., trauma, burn treatment, NICU, transplants, open heart surgery)

World Health Organization's Definition of Primary Health Care

- essential health care based on scientific methods
- universally accessible and acceptable
- affordable cost
- to maintain health at every developmental stage
- the first level of contact
- bringing health care as close as possible to where people live and work
- part of a continuing health care process

Institute of Medicine on the Future of Primary Care

- Primary care should be the
    - usual and preferred route of entry, but it is not the only route of entry into the system

    - The provision of integrated, accessible health care services by
        - clinicians who address health care needs, developing a partnership with patients, the family and community

Notes

Domains of Primary Care

- point of entry

- coordination of care

- essential care

- integrated care

- accountability

Domains of Primary Care

1. Point of Entry

- into the health care system where health care is organized around primary care
- the first contact a patient makes with the delivery system
- role of a gatekeeper
  - patients cannot see a specialist or be admitted without a physician referral
  - protect patients from unnecessary procedures and overtreatment
- goal:
  - bring it as close to the population as possible
  - "community-based"
  - convenience
  - accessible

Domains of Primary Care

2. Coordination of care

- Coordinate the delivery of health services between the patient and the myriad of components of the system
- Refer patients to sources of specialized care
- Give advice regarding various diagnosis and therapies
- To ensure continuity and comprehensiveness
- Discuss treatment options
- Provide continuing care of chronic conditions
  - See Figure 7-1

Domains of Primary Care

- Coordination of care

  - Countries with health systems oriented toward primary care
    - achieve better health levels,
    - higher satisfaction with health services
    - lower expenditures in the delivery of health
  - Countries with weak primary care infrastructures incur
    - poorer health outcomes and
    - higher health care costs

Domains of Primary Care

- Essential Care

  - Goal:
    - to optimize population health
    - disparities must be minimized to ensure equal access
  - In the United States,
    - public and private financing has created a fragmented system
      - primary care does not form the organizing hub for continuous and coordinated health services

Domains of Primary Care

- Integrated

  - comprehensive
    - it addresses health problems at any stage of a patient's life cycle

  - coordinated
    - combines health services to best meet the patient's needs

  - continuous services
    - care over time by a single provider or a team of health care professionals that provide a seamless process of care

Notes

Notes

Domains of Primary Care

• Accountability

- Clinicians and patients are accountable
- The clinical system is accountable for
  - providing quality care,
  - producing patient satisfaction,
  - using resources efficiently, and
  - behaving in an ethical manner
- Patients are responsible for
  - their own health to the extent of influencing it
  - being judicious in the use of resources

Domains of Primary Care

• Accountability

- Partnership between a patient and a clinician

- Mutual trust, respect, and responsibility are the hallmarks of this partnership

Community Oriented Primary Care

- The 1978 International Conference on Primary Health Care
  - concluded that people in the world had little control over their health
  - positive outcomes occur when people have ownership of programs that address their needs
  - requires a partnership between health providers and the communities

Notes

Community Oriented Primary Care

- Incorporates primary care with a population-based approach to identify and address community health problems

Community Oriented Primary Care

Requires four developments:

- Primary care must be central in delivery

- Biomedicine must include social and behavior sciences

- Primary and secondary prevention must be linked

- Public health must have clinical interventions in conjunction with:
  - schools, social service agencies, churches, and employers, to strengthen public health programs

Primary Care Effectiveness

- Preventive interventions should be carried out in primary care

- Continuity of care with one provider is positively associated with primary preventive care

- The likelihood that disadvantaged children will be brought for regular health visits is greater with a good primary provider

- Early detection of breast cancer is enhanced with an adequate supply of primary care physicians

Disease Management

Evidence exists that:

- hospitalizations for ambulatory care-sensitive conditions are less frequent when primary care is strong.

Costs of Care

- Where primary care is stronger, (where the primary care physician-to-population ratio is higher):
  - There are much lower total health care costs than in areas where there are fewer physicians.

Morbidity

Higher primary care physician supply has been associated with

- higher birth weights and

- lower infant mortality

- early detection of colorectal cancer

- better-controlled hypertension

Notes

Mortality

The supply of primary care physicians has been shown to have a direct influence on:

- life expectancy,
- stroke,
- postneonatal health and
- total mortality

Conclusion

- Ambulatory services transcend basic and routine primary care services

- General medical and surgical interventions are provided in ambulatory care settings

- Primary care is:
  - the point of entry into the health services system
  - where health care delivery is organized
  - essential

Conclusion

- A main function of primary care is to
  - coordinate the delivery of health services between the patient and the myriad of components of the system to maintain the long-term viability of a patient's health.
- Continuity of care over a period of time is essential
- Primary care is comprehensive
- Primary care plays a central role in a health care delivery system
  - it is linked to improved patient health status and cost-effectiveness

Notes

_____

Chapter 8

Hospitals

Introduction

- **Inpatient**
  - **requires an overnight stay in a health care facility**

- **Outpatient**
  - **services provided while the patient is <u>not</u> staying overnight in the hospital or some other health care institution**

Introduction

Hospital
- **an institution with at least 6 beds which functions to deliver patient services, diagnostics and treatment for medical conditions**
- **It must:**
  - **be licensed**
  - **have an organized physician staff**
  - **provide continuous nursing service under an Registered Nurse**
  - **have a governing body that is responsible for hospital conduct**
  - **have a CEO with responsibility for operations**

Introduction

The hospital must also:

– maintain medical records on each patient,

– have pharmacy services available

– provide food services to meet the nutritional and therapeutic requirements of the patients

Introduction

Construction and operations of a hospital are governed by:

– federal laws,

– state health department's regulations,

– city ordinances,

– JCAHO,

– fire codes, and

– sanitation

Introduction

- "Medical Center"

  – used by hospitals to reflect specialization and a large scope of services, including research

EVOLUTION OF THE HOSPITAL IN THE UNITED STATES

Before 1850,

– only a few hospitals were confined to some of the major U.S. cities.

– the main health care institutions were the almshouses or "poorhouses"

– their services were more like social welfare than medicine

EVOLUTION OF THE HOSPITAL IN THE UNITED STATES

After 1850,

– hospitals continued to serve mainly the poor, but

– hospitals were transitioning from primarily government institutions to community institutions

• supported mainly through private charitable donations

EVOLUTION OF THE HOSPITAL IN THE UNITED STATES

• During the latter half of the 19th century

-medical discoveries were instrumental in transforming hospitals into institutions of medical practice

-there were advances in anesthesia

-the germ theory of disease was developed, leading to the discovery of antiseptic and sterilization techniques for surgery

Notes

**EVOLUTION OF THE HOSPITAL
IN THE UNITED STATES**

- Hospitals
    - became necessities because superior medical services and procedures could not be obtained at home

    - began to attract well-to-do, private pay patients
        - no longer depending on charitable contributions, hospitals could generate a profit

- Physicians
    - started opening their own small hospitals, laying the foundation of proprietary (for profit) hospitals in the U.S.

**EVOLUTION OF THE HOSPITAL
IN THE UNITED STATES**

- Today's hospitals are complex organizations

- Hospital administration is a discipline in its own right.

- Administrators with expertise in financial management and organization are needed to manage hospitals

---

EVOLUTION OF THE HOSPITAL IN THE UNITED STATES

- Market pressures have prompted hospitals to merge or form affiliations
    - medical *systems* have formed
- Health systems may include more than one hospital
    - provide a full array of health care services
        - services can include:
            - outpatient clinics, same-day surgery, outpatient imaging services, outpatient rehabilitation therapies, nursing home care, home health, women's centers, fitness centers, community services such as health education, promotion of healthy lifestyles, and prevention of disease

EXPANSION AND DOWNSIZING OF HOSPITALS IN THE UNITED STATES

- Hospital beds grew from
  - 35,604 in 1872 to 907,133 in 1929

- Growth began as hospitals
  - served all of society
  - were able to make a profit
  - used surgical technologies that could only be utilized in hospitals

- After 1930, affordable insurance paid for services that were becoming more costly

EXPANSION AND DOWNSIZING OF HOSPITALS IN THE UNITED STATES

- Hospitals grew due to surgical procedures

- Health insurance generated new demand

- consumer behavior led to higher utilization of services

EXPANSION AND DOWNSIZING OF HOSPITALS IN THE UNITED STATES

In the 1940's, there was a shortage of hospitals, so...

- Congress passed the 1946 Hospital Survey and Construction Act ("The Hill Burton Act")

  - Federal grants were given to states for new community hospitals

  - The greatest factor to increasing the nation's bed supply

  - By 1980, 4.5 beds per 1,000 population were reached

Notes

Notes

**EXPANSION AND DOWNSIZING OF
HOSPITALS IN THE UNITED STATES**

Medicaid and Medicare were created in 1965

– made public health insurance available

– hospital demand continued to grow

• Between 1965 and 1980,
  –community hospitals increased from
    »5,736 (741,000 beds) to 5,830
    (988,000 beds)

**EXPANSION AND DOWNSIZING OF
HOSPITALS IN THE UNITED STATES**

In 1983, government decided to contain the cost of hospital care
– The Social Security Amendments of 1983 were enacted
  • The law required Medicare to stop paying hospitals per diem rates
    – a prospective payment system (PPS) was established to reimburse hospitals on the basis of diagnosis-related groups (DRGs)
– Hospitals received a pre-established fixed rate per admission.
  • In order not to lose money, they cut their costs of operation
    – Patients were discharged faster
– Hospitals closed because
  • they couldn't cope with the new reimbursement

**EXPANSION AND DOWNSIZING OF
HOSPITALS IN THE UNITED STATES**

• In the 1990s,
  – managed care curtailed inpatient utilization

• Managed care
  – emphasized early discharge, if necessary,
    • home health
    • skilled care
    • outpatient services

  • Look at Figure 8-2

**ACCESS AND UTILIZATION
BY THE U.S. POPULATION**

An indicator of access

- Definition: **the total number of patient
  discharges per 1,000 population for hospital
  inpatient services**
  - **newborn infants are not included in admissions**

**ACCESS AND UTILIZATION
BY THE U.S. POPULATION**

Discharges

- Definition: **total number of patients discharged
  from a hospital acute care bed in a given time
  period**

**ACCESS AND UTILIZATION
BY THE U.S. POPULATION**

Utilization

- **Inpatient Days**

  - **a night spent in the hospital by a person
    admitted as an inpatient**

- **Days of Care**
  - **the total number of inpatient days incurred by a
    population over a given time period**

Notes

ACCESS AND UTILIZATION
BY THE U.S. POPULATION

Average Length of Stay (ALOS)

= total days of care / total number of discharge

– measures how many days a patient on
average spends in the hospital

• Days of care = number of discharges x ALOS

ACCESS AND UTILIZATION
BY THE U.S. POPULATION

• Elderly spend more time in hospitals than do younger
people

• Women are admitted to hospitals more often than men

• Hospital utilization is higher among blacks than whites
and also among the poor than the nonpoor

• Overall hospital utilization is higher among Medicare
and Medicaid recipients

UTILIZATION OF
HOSPITAL CAPACITY

Capacity

– The number of beds set up, staffed and made
available by a hospital for inpatient use

– 84% of community hospitals in the U.S. have fewer
than 300 beds

– Rural hospitals have 65 beds on average

– Urban hospitals have 231 beds on average

**UTILIZATION OF
HOSPITAL CAPACITY**

- Census
  - the number of patients in a hospital on a given day

- Patient days
  - the cumulative census

- Average daily census
  - The average census over a given period of time
    - the average number of beds occupied per day

  Average daily census =
  patient days over a defined period ÷ number of days
  in the period

**UTILIZATION OF
HOSPITAL CAPACITY**

Occupancy rate

- the percent of capacity utilized during a
  defined period of time.

- derived by dividing the average daily census
  for that period by the capacity

- expressed as a percentage

- In 2001, the occupancy rate for all U.S.
  community hospitals was 64.5%.

Hospital Employment

12.6 million jobs in U.S. health care

- 42% or 5 million working in hospitals

- employment growth in hospitals will exceed 1%
  per year

- average hourly earning highest in hospitals
  - $18.63 for non-management workers

Notes

Types of Hospitals

- **Community**

- **Public**

- **Private Nonprofits**

- **Private For-Profit Hospitals**

  – A hospital can be classified in more than one category.

Types of Hospitals

Community

– a nonfederal short-stay hospital whose services are available to the general public

– approximately 85% are community hospitals

Types of Hospitals

Public
- connotes government ownership

- owned by federal, state or local governments

- approximately 18% of the U.S. hospital bed capacity
  - Look at Figure 8-3

- not always open to the general public

- Veterans Administration
  - the largest federal hospital system with 170 hospitals

Notes

Types of Hospitals

Public

- Often located in large urban areas
  - they serve mainly inner-city indigent and disadvantaged populations
  - have higher utilization
  - average size is 112 beds
  - offers a substantial amount of charity care
  - the number of state and local government-owned community hospitals declined by almost 20 percent between 1990 and 2000.

Types of Hospitals

Private Nonprofit Hospitals

- called *voluntary hospitals*

- nongovernment and privately-owned

- hospitals operate on a nonprofit basis

- operated by:
  - community associations
  - Churches
  - other nongovernment organizations

- the financial backing is done voluntarily by citizens without government help

Types of Hospitals

Private Nonprofit Hospitals

- 60% of all beds are private, nonprofits
  - Look at Figure 8-3

- Mission:

  - to benefit community where they're located

- Operating expenses covered by
  - patient fees, third party reimbursement, donations, endowments

Types of Hospitals

Private Nonprofit Hospitals
  – sometimes referred to as not-for-profit
  – Internal Revenue Code Section 501(c)(3)
    • grants tax-exempt status
    • exempt from federal, state and local taxes
      – income taxes, sales taxes, and property taxes
  – must provide:
    1) defined public good, service, education, welfare
    2) no profit to any individual
  – usually involved with community outreach
  – they provide charity, training, and/or research
  – whether nonprofit hospitals are charitable is controversial

Types of Hospitals

Private For Profit Hospitals
  – *proprietary hospitals*
    • also referred to as *investor-owned hospitals*
      – are owned by individuals, partnerships, or corporations for profit
  – operated for financial benefit to stockholders
  – a major goal for a for-profit organizations
    • to provide a return on investment to its shareholders

Types of Hospitals

General hospitals

    • Provide a variety and broad set of services for various conditions
      – general and specialized medical
      – obstetrics
      – diagnostics
      – treatment
      – surgery

    • Most hospitals in U.S. are general

Notes

Types of Hospitals

- **General hospitals are not less specialized or inferior to specialty hospital**

    - **difference is the nature of services, not quality**

    - **specialty has narrow range of services for specific conditions or patients**

Types of Hospitals

Specialty Hospitals

- **admits certain types of patients with certain illnesses**

- **can include psychiatric, rehabilitation, tuberculosis, children's hospitals**

- **emerging specialty hospitals:**
    - **orthopedic and cardiology**

- **provide a distinct service niche**

Types of Hospitals

Psychiatric Hospitals

- **provide diagnostic and treatment services for**
    - **patients who have psychiatric-related illnesses**

- **must have facilities to provide psychiatric, psychological, and social work services.**

- **must have a written agreement with a general hospital for the transfer of patients**

- **most mental health services are delivered in private psychiatric facilities and outpatient treatment centers**

Notes

_____
_____
_____
_____
_____
_____
_____
_____
_____
_____
_____
_____
_____
_____
_____
_____
_____
_____
_____
_____
_____
_____
_____
_____
_____
_____
_____
_____

Types of Hospitals

Rehabilitation Hospitals
- provide therapeutic service to restore maximum function in patients
- serve patients who generally cannot be cured but whose functioning can be improved
  - includes amputees, spinal cord or head injuries
    » accident or sport injuries
    » stroke victims
- treatment usually after orthopedic surgery
- provides PT, OT, speech, language pathology

Types of Hospitals

Children's Hospital

- **community-based**

- **facility designed for chronic, congenital cardiac and orthopedic pediatric problems**

- **usually provide strong rehabilitation programs**

Types of Hospitals

Rural hospitals

- are located in a county that is not part of a metropolitan statistical area (MSA)

- generally treat a larger percentage of poor and elderly patients.

- often find themselves in financial trouble and facing closure.

Notes

Types of Hospitals

Teaching Hospitals

- offer one or more graduate residency programs approved by the American Medical Association

- their primary role is to train physicians

- are either major or minor teaching institutions
  - a full teaching hospital should offer at a minimum, residencies in
    - general medicine, surgery, obstetrics and gynecology, and pediatrics

---

Types of Hospitals

Teaching Hospitals

- are usually affiliated with medical schools of large universities

- often operate several intensive care units

- possess the latest medical technologies

- attract specialists and

- offer tertiary care services, such as burn care, trauma care, and organ transplantation

---

Types of Hospitals

Osteopathic Hospitals

- for all practical purposes, they are community general hospitals

- have about 200 facilities in the United States

- use an approach to medical practice employing traditional methods associated with allopathic medicine, such as pharmaceuticals, laboratory tests, X-ray diagnostics, and surgery

Notes

_____

_____

_____

_____

_____

_____

_____

_____

_____

_____

_____

_____

_____

_____

_____

_____

_____

_____

_____

_____

_____

_____

_____

_____

_____

_____

_____

_____

_____

_____

_____

_____

_____

_____

_____

_____

_____

Types of Hospitals

Osteopathic medicine

- **takes a holistic approach**

- **advocates treatment that involves correction of the position of the joints or tissues**

- **emphasizes diet and environment to influence natural resistance**

Licensure, Certification
and Accreditation
  Licensure
    -state government oversees with own set of standards

    -must be licensed to operate

    -carried out by state departments of health

    -emphasizes physical plant compliance with:
      - building codes
      - fire safety
      - climate control
      - space allocations
      - sanitation

Licensure, Certification
and Accreditation

Certification

  – **Allows hospital to participate in Medicare and Medicaid**

  – **Department of Health and Hospitals Development "Conditions of Participation"**
    • **Department of Health and Hospitals contract with state departments to inspect**

**Licensure, Certification
and Accreditation**

Accreditation
- JCAHO evolved from ACS, AHA, AMA in 1951
- JCAHO
  - sets standards and accredits most:
    - general, long-term care, psychiatric hospitals
    - substance abuse programs
    - outpatient surgery centers
    - urgent care clinics
    - group practices
    - community health centers
    - hospice and home health agencies
    - labs

**Licensure, Certification
and Accreditation**

Accreditation

- Seeking accreditation is voluntary, but
  - Medicare specified that accredited facilities were eligible for purposes of reimbursement

- Facilities must also be certified by DHHS to receive
  - Medicare and Medicaid reimbursement.

- JCAHO has put greater emphasis on quality of care.

HOSPITAL ORGANIZATION

A hospital is generally responsible to:

- stakeholders such as

  - the community,
  - government,
  - insurers,
  - managed care organizations, and
  - accreditation agencies

Notes

HOSPITAL ORGANIZATION

- Internally, hospital governance involves three major sources of power
  - Board of Trustees
    - governing body, board of directors
  - CEO
    - receives delegated authority from the board and is responsible for managing the organization with the help of senior executives
      » nursing, rehabilitation, human resources, finance
  - Medical Staff

ETHICS AND PUBLIC TRUST

- The most significant ethical issues occur in acute care hospitals

- Physicians and caregivers are guided by the principles of *beneficence*
  - moral responsibilities when delivering clinical care

- *Nonmaleficence* means
  - providers have a moral obligation not to harm the patients

ETHICS AND PUBLIC TRUST

- A health services organization has an ethical obligation to
  - do all it can to alleviate suffering caused by ill health and injury

- Physicians encounter
  - legalized abortion, physician-assisted suicide, artificial prolongation of life, experimentation, and heroic measures to sustain a person's life

- Such issues do not have easy answers

Notes

ETHICS AND PUBLIC TRUST

Ethic Committees

  – charged with developing guidelines and
    standards for ethical decision-making in the
    provision of health care

  – interdisciplinary
    • involving physicians, nurses, clergy, social
      workers, legal experts, ethicists, and
      administrators

ETHICS AND PUBLIC TRUST

Addressing Ethical issues

• **The Patient Self-Determination Act of 1990**

  – applies to all health care facilities participating
    in Medicare or Medicaid

  – The law requires health care facilities to provide
    all patients, on admission, with information on
    patients' rights

ETHICS AND PUBLIC TRUST

Informed consent

  – a basic patient right

  – right to make an informed choice
    regarding medical treatment, including
    the right to refuse treatment

Notes

Advance Directives

- patient's wishes regarding continuation or withdrawal of treatment when patient lacks decision-making capacity

---

Public Trust

- Communities place a high degree of trust in their hospital
  - recent behavior of some hospitals has called trust into question.

- Hospital administrators have a fiduciary responsibility for acting prudently in managing the organization

- The hospital should be viewed as a community asset
  - when such a viewpoint is lost, a breach of public trust can occur.

Conclusion

- Any facility that treats patients on the basis of an overnight stay is called
  - an inpatient facility.

- The most common types of inpatient facilities are
  - hospitals and nursing homes

- Hospitals form the central core of health care delivery.

- Hospitals have been transformed into
  - integrated systems that deliver a full range of health care services.

Legal Rights

- Patient Bill of Rights
  - Patient Self-Determination Act of 1990

  - applies to all health care facilities accepting CMS

  - given to all patients on admission

  - covers:
    - confidentiality
    - consent
    - decisions regarding medical care
    - information on diagnostics and treatment
    - right to refuse treatment
    - formulation of advance directives

Legal Rights

- Patient Bill of Rights

- Informed Consent

- Advance Directives

- DNR

- Living will

- Durable power of attorney
  - Medical durable power of attorney

Notes

Notes

Chapter 9

Managed Care and
Integrated
Organizations

INTRODUCTION

Since around 1990,

- managed care has been the single most dominant force in the fundamental transformation of health care delivery in the United States.

- managed care experienced unprecedented success during the 1990's.

INTRODUCTION

- Employers began to realize savings

- Policymakers and administrators saw the opportunity to slow down the growing expense of providing health care

INTRODUCTION

■ Managed care has become firmly entrenched in the United States.

  – Some countries have adopted its features to reform their own traditional mechanisms of health care delivery.

■ Managed care was designed to control
  – quantity of health care and
  – the amount of reimbursement to providers

INTRODUCTION

■ Managed care organizations (MCOs) garnered great buying power by:

  – enrolling a large segment of the insured population and

  – taking responsibility to procure cost-effective health care for enrollees

What Is Managed Care?

■ Managed care is
  – a mechanism of providing health care services where a single organization takes on the management of financing, insurance, delivery, and payment.

  – MCOs exercise formal control over the utilization of health care services.

What Is Managed Care?

- The most common methods used for reimbursing providers are:

  – capitation and discounted fees.

What Is Managed Care?

- Capitation:
  – the provider is paid a fixed monthly sum per enrollee, often called a per member, per month (PMPM) payment.

- Discounted Fees:
  – a modified form of fee-for-service.
    - After services have been delivered, the provider can bill the MCO for each service separately but is paid according to a schedule of fees

What Is Managed Care?

Since 1991,

  – MCOs have been accredited by the

    - National Committee for Quality Assurance (NCQA).

What Is Managed Care?

- Health Plan Employer Data and Information Set (HEDIS) contains

    – the national standards and performance reports on individual MCOs

Evolution and Growth of Managed Care

- In the early 1900's,
    – railroad, mining, and lumber companies employed salaried physicians to provide care

- The Health Maintenance Organization Act of 1973
    – was passed to address escalating health care expenditures.
        – Look at Figure 9-1, page 201

Evolution and Growth of Managed Care

- During the 1980's,
    – managed care experienced slow growth, but
        - in California and Minnesota, growth was faster
            - Look at Figure 9-2, page 202

- As managed care grew, competition among MCOs gave rise to new forms of managed care

Evolution and Growth of Managed Care

Managed Care and Private Health Insurance

– Managed care
  ▪ now the primary vehicle for delivering health care to the majority of Americans.

Evolution and Growth of Managed Care

Managed Care and Private Health Insurance
  – Between 1990 and 2000,
    ▪ health insurance premiums for private employers grew 7%
      – as opposed to 12.2% between 1980 and 1990.
  – In 2002,
    ▪ 95% of Americans received employer-provided health benefits
    ▪ Only 27% received employer-provided benefits in 1988.

Evolution and Growth of Managed Care

▪ Managed Care & Public Health Insurance

  – enrolling Medicaid and Medicare beneficiaries into managed care has not been as successful

  – waivers under the Social Security Act,
    ▪ Sections 1115 and 1915 (b),
      – allowed states to enroll their Medicaid recipients in managed care plans.

Managed Care and Public Health Insurance

- Managed Care & Public Health Insurance

  - For Medicare beneficiaries,
    - managed care was an alternative to the fee-for-service program.

Managed Care and Public Health Insurance

In 1997,
  - the Balanced Budget Act,
    - created the Medicare+Choice program.

  - The program was enacted to increase Medicare enrollment into managed care.

Utilization Control Methods in Managed Care

MCOs use various methods to monitor and control the utilization of services.

1) an expert evaluation of what services are medically necessary in a case is required.

2) it requires providing services inexpensively while maintaining quality.

Utilization Control Methods in Managed Care

3) it requires a review of the process of care and changes in the patient's condition to revise the course of medical treatment.

Utilization Control Methods in Managed Care

- Gatekeeping

- Utilization Review
  - Prospective Utilization Review
  - Concurrent Utilization Review
  - Retrospective Utilization Review

Utilization Control Methods in Managed Care

Gatekeeping

- A method where a primary care physician coordinates all health services needed by an enrollee.

- It emphasizes
  - preventive care, routine physical examinations, and other primary care services

- Controls access to higher levels of care and hospitalizations

Utilization Control Methods in Managed Care

Utilization review

- the process of evaluating the appropriateness of services provided.

- its main objective is to review each case and determine the most appropriate level of services

Utilization Control Methods in Managed Care

Utilization review

- 3 types of utilization:

  ▪ Prospective Utilization Review

  ▪ Concurrent Utilization Review

  ▪ Retrospective Utilization Review

Utilization Control Methods in Managed Care

Prospective Utilization

- the medical necessity for certain treatments is determined before the care is delivered.

- One of the main objectives is to prevent unnecessary or inappropriate institutionalization or treatments, such as surgery.

Utilization Control Methods in Managed Care

Concurrent Utilization

– Making decisions regarding appropriateness of health care utilization.

– The most common example:
  ■ monitoring the length of inpatient stays

Utilization Control Methods in Managed Care

Concurrent Utilization
  – Discharge planning
    ■ important in concurrent utilization review.
    ■ Critical elements of review include
      – patient's prognosis, expected outcomes, and day of discharge
  – If a patient requires skilled nursing care
    ■ discharge planning must determine
      – the appropriate level of rehabilitation
      – how long insurance will pay for therapy in a long-term care setting.

Utilization Control Methods in Managed Care

Retrospective Utilization

– managing utilization after services have already been delivered.

– based on an examination of medical records to assess the appropriateness of care.

– Underutilization occurs when medically necessary care is not delivered.

Notes

_____

_____

_____

_____

_____

_____

_____

_____

_____

_____

_____

_____

_____

_____

_____

_____

_____

_____

_____

_____

_____

_____

_____

_____

_____

_____

_____

_____

_____

_____

_____

_____

_____

_____

_____

_____

_____

_____

_____

_____

Types of Managed Care Organizations

- HMOs
  - Staff Model
  - Group Model
  - Network Model
  - Independent Practice Association Model

- PPOs

- Exclusive Provider Organizations

- Point-of-Service Plans

Types of Managed Care Organizations

- Three factors that led to the development of different types of managed care plans
  - choice of providers
  - there are different ways of arranging services
  - payment and risk-sharing

Types of Managed Care Organizations

- HMOs
  - the most common type of MCOs in the 1970s,
    - HMOs had weaknesses; for example, poor choice of providers

- MCOs were developed to compete with restrictive HMOs by offering better choices

- Until about 1988, MCOs were distinct.

- Since then, the differences between traditional forms of health insurance and managed care have narrowed substantially.

Types of Managed Care Organizations

HMOs

- the first type of managed care plans to appear on the market.

- An HMO is distinguished from other types of plan by its focus on
  - wellness care,
  - capitation to pay providers, and
  - the use of in-network providers by enrollees

Types of Managed Care Organizations

HMOs

- Provide medical care during illness
- Offer a variety of services to help people maintain their health ("health maintenance")

- Emphasize prevention to save on health care costs in the long run

- Specialty services are "carved out"
  - "Carve outs" are a special contract outside capitation funded separately by the HMO

Types of Managed Care Organizations

HMOs

- There are four common HMO models.
  - Staff Model
  - Group Model
  - Network Model
  - Independent Practice Association Model
    - they differ according to the arrangements made with participating physicians.

Notes

Types of Managed Care Organizations

HMOs

    – Staff Model

        ■ A staff model HMO employs its own fixed salaried physicians, usually in common specialties

        ■ At the end of the year,

            – a pool of money is distributed among the physicians in the form of bonuses, based on each physician's productivity and the HMO's profitability

Types of Managed Care Organizations

HMOs

    – Staff Model

        ■ Exercises greater control over practice patterns and can better monitor utilization

        ■ The least popular type of HMO
            – continues to decline because of
                ■ high operating expenses and limited choice

Types of Managed Care Organizations

HMOs

    – Group Model
        ■ Contracts with a multispecialty group practice,
            – and separately with one or more hospitals, to provide comprehensive services to its member.
        ■ Physicians are employed by the practice, not the HMO
        ■ The HMO pays an all-inclusive capitation fee to the practice to provide physician services to its enrollees
        ■ May be an independent practice

Types of Managed Care Organizations

HMOs

– Network Model

- the HMO contracts with more than one medical group practice.
- adaptable to large metropolitan areas and widespread geographic regions where group practices are located
- the group is responsible for providing all physician services
- able to offer more choice
- disadvantage: dilution of utilization control

Types of Managed Care Organizations

HMOs

– Independent Practice Association (IPA) Model

- has been the most successful in terms of enrollment
  - has the largest share of enrollments and maintaining the number of enrollments over time.
- the IPA establishes contracts with solo and group practices
- the IPA functions as an intermediary representing many physicians

Types of Managed Care Organizations

HMOs

– Independent Practice Association (IPA) Model

- the HMO is responsible for providing services to its enrollees,
  the administrative and contracting functions are shifted to the IPA.
- Provides an expanded choice of providers
- Allows small physician groups to be a part of managed care
- Disadvantage: If a contract is lost, the HMO loses a large percentage of participating physicians

Notes

_____

_____

_____

_____

_____

_____

_____

_____

_____

_____

_____

_____

_____

_____

_____

_____

_____

_____

_____

_____

_____

_____

_____

_____

_____

_____

_____

_____

_____

_____

_____

Types of Managed Care Organizations

PPOs

   – PPOs differentiate themselves by offering out-of-network options for enrollees.

   – Enrollees agree to use preferred providers with whom the PPO has contracts, but the patient is also allowed to use providers outside the network

      – Patients pay higher copays for out-of-network service

Types of Managed Care Organizations

PPOs

   – Instead of capitation, PPOs make discounted fee arrangements with providers.

      ■ discounts range between 25% - 35% off providers' regular fees.

Types of Managed Care Organizations

Exclusive Providers Organizations (EPOs)

   – Similar to PPOs in its organization and purpose

   – Enrollees, however, are restricted to the list of preferred providers called "exclusive providers."

   – Uses gatekeeping

   – Implemented mostly by employers where cost savings is the goal

Types of Managed Care Organizations

Point-of-Service (POS) Plans

- POS plans combine features of HMOs with patient choice found in PPOs.

- POS plans overcome restricted provider choice but retain the benefits of tight utilization

- Free choice of providers is a major selling point for POS

- POS peaked in 1998-1999, but has declined due to high out-of-pocket costs

Impact on Cost, Access, and Quality

- Influence on Cost Containment

- Impact on Access

- Influence on Quality Care

Impact on Cost, Access, and Quality

Influence on Cost Containment

- In the United States,
  - the primary responsibility for cost containment falls on the private sector using managed care
    - government uses various methods to control Medicaid and Medicare costs.

- Health premiums in 2001-2002 rose 12.7%
  - employers will seek help by cost sharing and managing utilization

Notes

Impact on
Cost, Access, and Quality

Impact on Access

- Managed care enrollees usually have good access to
  - primary care, preventive services, and health promotion activities.

- The quality of health care provide by MCOs has improved over time
  - early detection and treatment is more likely in managed care than fee-for-service

Impact on
Cost, Access, and Quality

Influence on Quality of Care

- Managed care has been cost-effective, by lowering the use of hospital and expensive resources

- Findings, though, point to lower access and lower enrollee satisfaction for HMOs compared to non-HMOs

Impact on
Cost, Access, and Quality

Influence on Quality of Care

- A comprehensive literature review by Miller and Luft (2002) concluded that
  - HMO and non-HMO plans provided equal quality care

- Managed care has prevented racial disparities in quality of care

Health Networks

- With managed care's growth, MCOs acquired power

  - the bargaining power of independent organizations, such as hospitals and clinics, was eroding.

- Organizations had pressure to reduce costs, which was hard for small providers

  - networks became a rational choice for survival

Health Networks

- Integrated health care organizations are often referred to as integrated delivery systems or health networks

- Integrated delivery systems are formed mostly by large hospitals

- Joint ventures, alliances and affiliations combine resources to serve large communities

- Large organizations sometimes
  - create their own managed care plans or contract with large employers for one-stop shop health plans

Health Networks

- A fully integrated health network typically includes:

  - One or more acute care hospitals

  - Ambulatory care facilities

  - One or more physician group practices

  - One or more long-term care facilities

  - Home health services

  - Ownership or contract with one or more MCOs

Health Networks

Organizational integration has:

– enabled hospitals to expand into new markets.

– intensified competition among health care providers.

– enabled large health service organizations to win sizeable managed care contracts or to offer their own health plans.

– become more complex and difficult to manage

Health Networks

■ There are about 600 health networks operating in the United States

– nearly half of all acute care hospitals are affiliated with some integrated network.

Types of Integration

• Integration Based on Major Participants

• Integration Based on Ownership or Affiliation
   • Acquisitions and Mergers
   • Joint Ventures
   • Alliances
   • Virtual Organizations

• Integration Based on Service Consolidation
   • Vertical Integration

Types of Integration

Integration Based on Major Participants

- Physicians and hospitals are two key participants in integrated organizations
    - one entity usually cannot function without the other.
    - hence, physician-hospital organizations (PHOs) have been a common type of integration
    - A PHO is a
    - legal entity that forms an alliance between a hospital and local physicians that combine their services within one organization.

Types of Integration

- The PHO allows both entities to have greater bargaining power to contract negotiations with MCOs.

- Large PHOs can contract directly with employers

- PHOs provide the benefits of integration while preserving independence and autonomy.

- About 2,300 hospitals/systems and 152,000 physicians have formed PHOs

Types of Integration

- Integration Based on Type of Ownership or Affiliation
    - Owner involves the purchase of a controlling interest in another company,
        - Done either through a merger or an acquisition.
    - It may simply involve cooperative arrangements and joint responsibilities.
    - They share resources among the various organizations based on contracts.

Types of Integration

- Integration Based on Type of Ownership or Affiliation

  - Acquisitions and Mergers
    - Acquisition refers to the purchase of one organization by another.
    - Mergers involve a mutual agreement unifying two or more organizations into a single entity.
    - The separate assets brought together are put under a new name

Types of Integration

- Integration Based on Type of Ownership or Affiliation

  - Acquisitions and Mergers

    - The former entities cease to exist, and a new corporation is formed.

    - Acquisitions and merges can also help an organization expand into new geographic markets.

Types of Integration

- Integration Based on Type of Ownership or Affiliation

  - Joint Ventures
    - Result when two or more institutions share resources to create a new organization to pursue a common purpose.
    - Each of the participants in a joint venture continues to conduct business independently.
    - Used to diversify services by joining instead of competing

Types of Integration

- Integration Based on Type of Ownership or Affiliation

  - Alliances
    - an agreement between two organizations to share their resources without joint ownership of assets.

    - Cooperation instead of competition
      - eliminates duplication of services while ensuring that all the health needs of the community are fulfilled.

Types of Integration

- Integration Based on Type of Ownership or Affiliation
  - Virtual Organizations
    - are contractual arrangements between organizations that form a new organization
    - Virtual integration is the formation of networks based on contractual arrangements
    - IPAs are a prime example of virtual organization
    - PHOs can be a virtual organization
    - The main advantage of virtual organizations is that they require less capital to enter new geographic or service markets.

Types of Integration

- Integration Based on Service Consolidation

  - Horizontal Integration

    - Is a growth strategy in which a health care delivery organization extends its core product or service.

    - The main objective of horizontal integration is to achieve geographic expansion.

Notes

Types of Integration

- Integration Based on Service Consolidation

  - Vertical Integration
    - Links services that are at different stages in the production process of health care
    - Its purpose is to increase the comprehensiveness and continuity of care
    - It is a diversification strategy
    - Can be achieved through acquisitions, mergers, joint ventures or alliances.

Conclusion

- Most Americans receive care through managed care

- Cost savings were achieved while quality was maintained

- New concerns are about the ability of managed care to control costs

Conclusion

- Health networks emerged as hospitals and physicians faced pressures from managed care to cut costs

- Integration allowed large health organizations to win sizeable insurance plans

- Integrating physicians into large organizations is challenging.

Notes

Chapter 10

Long-Term Care
Services

Introduction

Long-term Care (LTC)

- is often associated with care provided in nursing homes
  - a narrow view
  - the majority of services are provided in community-based settings

- is usually done with informal care by the family
  - two out of five elderly LTC users rely solely on informal care

  - social support networks have a positive effect on physical and mental functioning status, forestalling institutionalization

Introduction

LTC includes:

- home health brought to a person's home

- home delivered meals

- minimal assistance in residential settings

Introduction

- LTC is not confined to the elderly, but
  - they are the predominant users
  - LTC services are built with the elderly in mind, however
    - it is incorrect to presume that most elderly are in need of such care
- Most older persons are physically and mentally healthy enough to live independently.
- According to surveys of the civilian noninstitutionalized population,
  - 73% of elderly assessed their own health status as "good," "very good," or "excellent."

Introduction

- Aging leads to chronic, degenerative conditions that resist cure.

- Those over age 65
  - consume one-third of all national health care spending, although they represent only about 13% of the U.S. population,
  - occupy one-half of all physician time

- Therefore, utilization of health care services is
  - much higher among older adults than among younger persons

---

Introduction

LTC
  - must be closely related to the health care delivery system
  - associated with <u>chronic conditions</u>:
    - persistent and recurring health consequences that exist over a long period and are usually irreversible
      - examples include Arthritis, diabetes, asthma, heart disease, cancer, and dementia
    - the leading cause of illness, disability and death
  - a person's age, chronic ailments, **comorbidity** (multiple health problems), disability, and dependency tend to follow each other

    - Look at Figure 10-1

Introduction

- Between 2000 and 2020,
  - Americans with chronic conditions is
    - projected to increase from 125 million (45 percent of the population) to 157 million

- Although institutionalization among the elderly has been falling
  - this trend will likely reverse itself within ten years, pointing to a growing need for nursing home care in the future

What is Long-term Care?

It's a variety of services that are

- well-coordinated to promote the maximum possible independence for people with functional limitations, and are provided over an extended period of time to

  −meet the patients' physical, mental, social, and spiritual needs while maximizing their quality of life.

What is Long-term Care?

Seven Characteristics of Long-Term Care

1. It must include a variety of health care services.
2. Services must be well-coordinated.
3. Services are designed for the functionally-impaired.
4. The goal is to promote maximum possible independence.
5. Services are needed over an extended period of time.
6. Patients' physical, mental, social, and spiritual needs must be met.
7. Patients' quality of life must be maximized.

Notes

Notes

What is Long-term Care?

1. It must include a variety of health care services

   • need varies greatly from individual to individual

   • long term care includes:
     • housing programs,
     • transportation,
     • case management,
     • recreation,
     • nutrition, and
     • various types of social support services

What is Long-term Care?

1. It must include a variety of health care services.

   – the need for the types of services change and fluctuate over time

   – LTC must also include both therapeutic and preventive services
     • The primary goal of preventive services is to prevent or delay the need for institutionalization

   – social support programs are also a preventive function
     • programs such as homemaker, chore, and handyman services
       – Examples include shopping, light cleaning, general errands, lawn maintenance, and minor home repairs.

What is Long-term Care?

2. Services must be well-coordinated.

   – Availability and variety of services
     • may not be enough to meet the changing needs--unless they are well-coordinated

     • the health care delivery system can be difficult to navigate
       –difficulties compound in case of the elderly and disabled

Notes

What is Long-term Care?

3. Services are designed for the functionally impaired
   - when people's capacities are diminished
     - chronic conditions and comorbidity make some not able to complete tasks for themselves, such as activities of daily living
       - **Activities of daily living (ADL):**
         - bathing or showering,
         - dressing and grooming,
         - eating,
         - walking
         - transferring
         - maintaining bowel and bladder control
     Functional impairment is:
       - A person's lack of ability to perform common activities
       - Look at Figure 10-1

What is Long-term Care?

3. Services are designed for the functionally impaired
   - **Instrumental activities of daily living (IADL)**
     - A measure of physical function
     - It measures activities necessary for living independently such as:
       - using the telephone,
       - driving a car or traveling alone on a bus or taxi,
       - shopping,
       - preparing meals,
       - doing light housework,
       - taking medicine,
       - handling money,
       - doing heavy housework,
       - walking stairs, and
       - walking a half mile without help
     - 40 percent of the elderly have some functional limitations with ADLs or IADLs

What is Long-term Care?

4. The goal: To promote maximum possible independence

   - Restoration of function may be possible with equipment such as:
     - wheelchairs, walkers, special eating utensils, or portable oxygen devices

   - Caregivers motivate and help the patient do as much as possible for him or herself.

Notes

What is Long-term Care?

5. Services are needed over an extended period of time.

- Compared to acute care, LTC is sustained over a longer period of time

  • may be indicated for a short period, generally lasting 90 days or less

- It is not uncommon for LTC to be initiated in a nursing home

---

What is Long-term Care?

6. Patients' physical, mental, social, and spiritual needs must be met

- Health care focuses on physical aspects

- Mental health is an integral part of LTC

- In long-term care, the holistic model must prevail

What is Long-term Care?

6. Patients' physical, mental, social, and spiritual needs must be met
   Four aspects of holistic caregiving:
   1. Physical:
      • technical aspects of care, such as
        – Medical examination, nursing care, medications, diet, rehabilitation treatments, comfort factors, such as temperature and cozy furnishings, cleanliness, and safety in an institutional environment.
   2. Mental:
      – layout, décor, and techniques that help overcome disorientation and confusion;
      – mental stimulation to help overcome boredom and depression;
      – an environment that promotes positive feelings with
        • live plants, flowers, water, pleasant aromas, and soothing music

---

What is Long-term Care?

3. Social:
  – nursing homes have created indoor and outdoor spaces such as:
    • game rooms, alcoves, balconies, and patios where people can enjoy each other's company.

4. Spiritual:
  – personal beliefs, values, and commitments in a religious and faith context.

  – Requires interaction with other members of the faith community.

What is Long-term Care?

7. Patients' quality of life must be maximized.

• **Quality of life**
  – the total living experience that results in overall satisfaction with one's life.

  – recognizes at least five factors:
    • lifestyle pursuits,
    • living environment,
    • clinical palliation,
    • human factors, and
    • personal choices

What is Long-term Care?

7. Patients' quality of life must be maximized.
Quality of life
  – lifestyle pursuits
    • personal enrichment, making life meaningful through activities one enjoys
  – living environment,
    • comfortable, safe, and appealing to the senses.
    • cleanliness, décor, furnishings, and other aesthetic features
  – clinical palliation
    • relief from unpleasant symptoms such as pain or nausea
  – human factors
    • caregiver attitudes and practices that emphasize caring, compassion, and preservation of human dignity
  – personal choices
    • offering a selection of dishes

Notes

Notes

COMMUNITY-BASED
LONG-TERM CARE SERVICES

Objectives of community-based LTC Services:

(1) to supplement informal caregiving where
  – more advanced skills are needed to address the patients' needs,

(2) to provide respite to family members from caregiving stress

(3) to delay or prevent institutionalization by
  – meeting the needs of the most vulnerable elderly in community settings

COMMUNITY-BASED
LONG-TERM CARE SERVICES

Elderly services offered through an administrative network that includes:

  – the Federal Administration on Aging,

  – State Units on Aging, and

  – Area Agencies on Aging.

• Nationally, 670 Area Agencies on Aging administer funds appropriated by the federal government under the Older Americans Act of 1965.

COMMUNITY-BASED
LONG-TERM CARE SERVICES

For the financially-needy, Title III of the Older Americans Act may finance such community-based services as:

1. Home Maintenance

2. Adult Day Care

3. Health promotion and disease prevention

4. Nutrition and meals

5. Telephone reassurance

6. Transportation services

COMMUNITY-BASED LONG-TERM CARE SERVICES

1. Home health care

   – health care provided in the home of the patient
- To qualify for home care under the Medicare program,
  – patients must be homebound,
  – patients must have a plan of treatment periodically reviewed by a physician
  – require intermittent or part-time skilled nursing and/or rehabilitation therapies

- Private payers prefer to minimize the high costs of hospital inpatient care and opt for home health services wherever possible

COMMUNITY-BASED LONG-TERM CARE SERVICES

Home health services can include:
- nursing care, such as
  - changing dressings, monitoring medications, and bathing
- short-term rehabilitation, such as
  - physical therapy, occupational therapy, and speech therapy
- homemaker services, such as
  - meal preparation, shopping, transportation, and some household chores;
- certain medical supplies and equipment, such as
  - ostomy supplies, hospital beds, oxygen tanks, walkers, and wheelchairs.
- Not all home health agencies provide all of these services

COMMUNITY-BASED LONG-TERM CARE SERVICES

2. Adult Day Care

   – a daytime program of nursing care, rehabilitation therapies, supervision, and socialization that enables frail (usually elderly) people to remain in the community

   – a type of respite program that gives family caregivers time to fulfill other responsibilities.

Notes

**COMMUNITY-BASED
LONG-TERM CARE SERVICES**

2. Adult Day Care

- The National Adult Day Services Association (NADSA),
  defined ADC

    - a community-based group program designed to

        • meet the needs of functionally and/or cognitively impaired
          adults through an individual plan of care

    - less than 24-hour care

    - normal business hours, five days a week

    - some programs offer services in the evenings and on weekends

---

**COMMUNITY-BASED
LONG-TERM CARE SERVICES**

3. Adult Foster Care

    - Small, family-run homes providing

        • room, board, and varying levels of supervision, oversight,
          and personal care to

            - adults who are unable to care for themselves

    - To maintain the family environment, most states license fewer
      than 10 beds per family unit.

    - Each state has established its own standards for the licensing of
      foster care homes

**COMMUNITY-BASED
LONG-TERM CARE SERVICES**

4. Senior Centers
    - local community centers for older adults.
    - places where seniors can congregate and socialize
- Many centers offer:
    - one or more meals daily.
    - wellness programs,
    - health education,
    - counseling services
    - recreational activities,
    - information and referral, and
    - some limited health care services, including:
        • health screening, especially for glaucoma and hypertension
- Nearly all senior centers receive some public funding

COMMUNITY-BASED LONG-TERM CARE SERVICES

5. Home delivered Meals
- The Elderly Nutrition Program (ENP) operates under the U.S. Administration on Aging to
  - serve congregate and home-delivered meals.
- The goal of this program is to:
  - improve the dietary intake of older Americans (60 years and older)
  - offer participants opportunities to form new friendships and
  - create informal support networks.
- One hot noon meal five days a week to those who are unable to prepare a nutritionally-balanced noon meal for themselves
- Referred to as **meals-on-wheels**
  - volunteers deliver the meals and are encouraged to spend some time with the elderly

COMMUNITY-BASED LONG-TERM CARE SERVICES

6. Homemaker Services
- simple tasks necessary for independent living
  - grocery shopping,
  - household chores, and
  - handyman services
  - light cleaning,
  - general errands, and
  - minor home repairs.
- Homemaker programs may be staffed largely or entirely by volunteers

COMMUNITY-BASED LONG-TERM CARE SERVICES

7. Emergency Response and Telephone Reassurance
- a Personal Emergency Response System (PERS),
  - also called a Medical Emergency Response System
    - an electronic device that enables people to summon help
      - designed for disabled or elderly people who live alone
- Person wears or carries a transmitter that enables the individual to send a medical alert to a local 24-hour monitoring and response center.

Notes

Notes

**COMMUNITY-BASED
LONG-TERM CARE SERVICES**

8. Case Management

- a method of linking, managing, and coordinating services to meet the varied and changing health care needs of elderly clients
  - to prepare a care plan to address those needs,
  - to identify services that are most appropriate,
  - to determine eligibility for services,
  - to make referrals and coordinate delivery of care,
  - to arrange for financing, and
  - to ensure that clients are receiving services

Institutional Long-term Care

- For patients whose needs cannot be adequately met in a less acute, community-based setting

- Institutional options meet the varying needs of the elderly in:
  - retirement centers,
  - residential or personal care facilities
  - assisted living facilities

- These facilities provide varying levels of assistance
  - Look at Figure 10-2

Institutional Long-term Care

Continuing Care Retirement Community

- Three main segments of institutional long-term care
  - retirement and residential living apartments or cottages,
  - personal care
  - assisted living services
    - different levels of service are available in adjoining buildings
- A separate skilled nursing facility provides
  - intermittent and permanent accommodations based on changing needs
- Based on the concept of aging-in-place,
  - people's changing needs are met while their independence is preserved

---

Institutional Long-term Care

Retirement or Independent Living Facility

- not considered long-term care institutions
- nursing care services not provided
  - but privacy, security, independence, and active lifestyles emphasized

- facilities organize programs for
  - socializing, physical fitness, recreation, shopping and entertainment

- some offer **hotel services** such as:
  - one meal a day and periodic housekeeping

Institutional Long-term Care

Retirement or Independent Living Facility

- Apartment units or detached cottages are offered
  - equipped with kitchenettes and private baths
  - common laundry rooms
  - government subsidizes housing units for low-income elderly and disabled

- Many upscale retirement facilities have
  - substantial entrance fee plus a monthly rental or maintenance fee.

Institutional Long-term Care

- Residential or Personal Care Facilities
  - non-medical custodial care
    - basic assistance provided in a protected environment

      –does not require active medical or rehabilitative treatments that would improve health or function.

- The focus is on providing routine assistance with ADLs.

Notes

Notes

Institutional Long-term Care
Residential or Personal Care Facilities

- Have different names such as:
  - domiciliary care facilities,
  - board-and-care homes,
  - foster care homes,
  - residential care facilities, or
  - personal care facilities.
- They provide:
  - physically supportive dwelling units,
  - monitoring and/or assistance with medications,
  - oversight,
  - light assistance with certain ADLs such as bathing and grooming

Institutional Long-term Care
Assisted Living Facilities

- the fastest growing long-term care institution in the United States.
- a residential setting that provides:
  - personal care services,
  - 24-hour supervision,
  - scheduled and unscheduled assistance,
  - social activities, and
  - some nursing care services
  - some ADL assistance
    - **bathing, dressing, and toileting.**
  - help with medications
- these facilities border between personal care homes and nursing homes
- there are approximately 33,000 assisted living residences, housing about 800,000 people

Institutional Long-term Care
Skilled Nursing Facility

- provides a full range of clinical long-term care services
  - from skilled nursing care, rehabilitation to assistance with all ADLs
- **Skilled nursing care** is
  - medically oriented care provided by a licensed nurse
    - The plan of treatment is authorized by a physician
    - Most direct care is delivered by paraprofessionals
      - **but under the supervision of licensed nurses and therapist**
- Rehabilitation, therapeutic diets and nutritional supplements are important components of skilled care
- The patient's treatment plan is individualized

Institutional Long-term Care

Sub acute care

- a blend of intensive medical, nursing, and other services
- substitutes for services previously provided in acute hospitals
  - it is a cheaper alternative to a hospital stay
- patients may still be unstable requiring
  - monitoring and treatment, or
  - technically complex nursing, such as:
    - wound care, intravenous therapy, blood transfusion, or AIDS care
- generally follows hospitalization required for a relatively short-period of time
    - between 20 and 90 days

Institutional Long-term Care

Sub acute care

- Services are generally delivered by:
  (1) Long-term care units
    - known as transitional care units (TCUs) or extended care units (ECUs),
      - both are located in acute care hospitals

  (2) Nursing homes
    - hire additional registered nurses and therapists

  (3) Community-based home health agencies
    - care provided in a patient's own home.

Licensing, Certification, and Accreditation of Nursing Homes

- Nursing homes are heavily regulated through licensure and certification requirements

- It is illegal to operate a nursing facility without a license

Notes

Notes

Licensing, Certification, and Accreditation of Nursing Homes

Nursing Home License
- A **license** allows a facility to operate and do business
- Every state requires nursing homes to be licensed by the state
  - states can control the total number of nursing home beds
    - annual renewal of their licenses is required
    - license must be displayed in a public area
- To keep their licenses in good standing, facilities must ensure compliance with the:
  - **Life Safety Code**
    - encompasses national building and fire safety rules
    - often referred to as NFPA 101, is published by the National Fire Protection Association

Licensing, Certification, and Accreditation of Nursing Homes

Certification of Nursing Homes
- **Certification** allows a nursing home to admit patients who are on public assistance
- Nursing homes must first be licensed by the state
- To serve Medicaid and/or Medicare clients,
  - The home must be certified by the Centers for Medicare and Medicaid Services (CMS),
- It is possible for a facility to only have a license, not receive reimbursement from CMS for their clients

Licensing, Certification, and Accreditation of Nursing Homes

Three distinct federal certification categories

1. **Skilled Nursing Facility certification** (SNF)

   - allows a facility to admit Medicare patients

   - pays for only post-acute nursing home care after a patient has stayed in a hospital for a minimum of three days

   - The maximum coverage is 100 days

   - People receive an average of 23 days of care per admission

Licensing, Certification, and Accreditation of Nursing Homes

Three distinct federal certification categories

2. **Nursing Facility certification** (NF)
   - allows a facility to admit Medicaid patients
   - allows patients to stay in a NF-certified nursing home indefinitely, as long as the physician authorizes the need
   - The beneficiary is required to turn over most of his or her monthly income to the facility; Medicaid pays the remaining costs.
   - Patients initially admitted to a facility with private pay
     - When private funds are exhausted, patients can be eligible for Medicaid
   - A facility may be dually certified, as both a SNF and a NF.
   - Facilities having **dual certification** can admit Medicare and/or Medicaid patients to any part of the facility.

Licensing, Certification, and Accreditation of Nursing Homes

Three distinct federal certification categories

3. **ICF/MR (Intermediate Care Facility for the Mentally Retarded) certification**
   - allows a nursing facility to serve patients who are mentally retarded/developmentally disabled.

   - **Developmental disability** is a
     - physical incapacity that generally accompanies mental retardation
     - often arises at birth or in early childhood

Licensing, Certification, and Accreditation of Nursing Homes

Accreditation
   - a private function; it's voluntary
   - The Joint Commission on Accreditation of Healthcare Organizations (Joint Commission or JCAHO)—a private non-profit organization—accredits:
     - hospitals, nursing homes, and other health care facilities
   - Few nursing facilities have opted to seek accreditation
     - accreditation fees are high compared to benefits gained
     - It's onerous to have an extra layer of standards to comply with
   - Accreditation has advantages
     - There is a high degree of correlation between accreditation and performance
       - accredited facilities perform better on quality measures, and
       - have reduced exposure to malpractice lawsuits

Notes

_____

_____

_____

_____

_____

_____

_____

_____

_____

_____

_____

_____

_____

_____

_____

_____

_____

_____

_____

_____

_____

_____

_____

_____

_____

_____

_____

_____

_____

_____

_____

_____

_____

_____

_____

_____

_____

_____

_____

_____

OTHER LONG-TERM CARE SERVICES

1. Respite

   – The most frequently suggested intervention to address family caregivers' feeling of stress and burden.

   – Virtually any kind of service—adult day care [ADC], home health care, and temporary institutionalization—
     • can be viewed as respite care as long as the focus is on giving informal caregivers some time off while meeting disabled persons' needs for assistance

OTHER LONG-TERM CARE SERVICES

2. Restorative Care
   – caregiving in which patients are viewed as participants capable of reaching their maximum potential in physical and mental functioning.

   – services include but go beyond the rehabilitative therapies, such as range of motion exercises, bowel and bladder training, and assisted walking

   – services provided by:
     • home health agencies, rehabilitation hospitals, outpatient rehabilitation clinics, adult day care centers, and assisted living and skilled nursing facilities (SNFs).

OTHER LONG-TERM CARE SERVICES

3. Hospice
     • is cluster of comprehensive services for the terminally ill who have a life expectancy of six months or less
   – It blends medical, spiritual, legal, financial, and family-support services.
   – It is a method of care, not a location
   – It can be a part of home health care when the services are provided in:
     • the patient's home
     • nursing homes,
     • retirement centers, or
     • hospitals.
   – The objective is maintaining the patient's dignity and comfort

OTHER LONG-TERM CARE SERVICES

3. Hospice

- emphasizes **palliative care**
  - comfort and pain management and social support over medical intervention

- arranges spiritual counseling and legal assistance with wills and estates.

- means that temporary measures to prolong life will be suspended.

STATE OF THE NURSING HOME INDUSTRY

- The number of nursing homes and beds have been gradually increasing
  - but the use of these beds has declined
    - Look at Table 10-2

- A growing population with chronic conditions, comorbidities, and subsequent disability will need nursing home care.

- The industry is dominated by private for-profit nursing homes.
  - 2/3 are proprietary for-profit,
  - 27% are private non-profit
  - 7% percent are government owned, mostly owned and operated by local counties

STATE OF THE NURSING HOME INDUSTRY

- Medicaid
  - the main source of financing for nursing home care, paying nearly half of all expenditures
- Medicare
  - pays for eligible beneficiaries under Part A, but the coverage is for a short duration.
- LTC policies
  - expensive and cover only a portion of the total expenses
    - less than 10 percent of people age 50 and over purchase LTC insurance

  - Look at Table 10-3.

Notes

Notes

_____

_____

_____

_____

_____

_____

_____

_____

_____

_____

_____

_____

_____

_____

_____

_____

_____

_____

_____

_____

_____

_____

_____

_____

_____

_____

_____

_____

_____

_____

_____

_____

Conclusion

- The need for long-term care is closely associated with functional impairment.

- LTC may be needed at any age, but the elderly are the largest users
  - because aging leads to chronic and degenerative conditions that cause the elderly to lose at least some physical and mental function

- Those with some limitations can rely on a variety of services available in the community.

- Only those who require 24-hour nursing care need to be in a nursing home

Conclusion

- To operate as a nursing home, the facility must be licensed by the state.

- To admit Medicare and Medicaid patients, it must also have federal certification.

- Unless a facility is certified, it can admit only those patients who can pay privately.

- With the aging of the baby boom population,
  - long-term care services are expected to grow at a rapid rate, beginning around 2015.

Chapter 11: Underserved Populations

Notes

Chapter 11

Underserved
Populations

Introduction

- Certain populations in the United States
  - face greater challenges in accessing timely and need health care services.

- They are at risk for
  - poor physical, psychological and/or social health

- They are called
  - underserved populations
  - medically underserved
  - medically disadvantaged
  - underprivileged
  - American underclasses

Introduction

- Their vulnerability is due to:
  - Unequal social, economic, health and geographic conditions
  - They consists of:
    - Racial and ethnic minorities
    - Uninsured children
    - Women
    - Those living in rural areas
    - Homeless
    - Mentally ill
    - Chronically ill and disabled
    - HIV/AIDS patients

Notes

Framework To Study Vulnerable Populations

- Racial / Ethnic Minorities

- Women and Children

- Geographical Distribution: Rural Health

Framework To Study Vulnerable Populations

- Vulnerability Model
  - an integrated approach to studying vulnerability
    - Look at Figure 11.1, page 248

- Vulnerability
  - denotes susceptibility to negative events

- In health care, vulnerability is the
  - likelihood of experiencing poor health or illness

Framework To Study Vulnerable Populations

- Poor health is compounded for problems along multiple dimensions

- Vulnerability represents the interaction effects of multiple factors over which many do not have control

Framework To Study
Vulnerable Populations

- Vulnerability is determined by a convergence of:
  - predisposing
  - enabling
  - need
    - characteristics at both individual and ecological level
  - They converge and determine access to care and influence individuals' risk of contracting illness
    - Look at Exhibit 11.1, page 249

Framework To Study
Vulnerable Populations

- Understanding vulnerability as a combination or convergence of disparate factors is preferred over studying individual factors separately

Framework To Study
Vulnerable Populations

- The vulnerability model has distinctive characteristics:
  - 1. It is comprehensive,
    - including individual and ecological attributes of risk.
  - 2. It focuses on the attributes of vulnerability for the total population
    - rather than on vulnerable traits of subpopulations.

Notes

Framework To Study Vulnerable Populations

- 3. It emphasizes the convergence of vulnerability.

- Multiple vulnerable traits may lead to
  - cumulative vulnerability that is additive or multiplicative

Framework To Study Vulnerable Populations

- Attributes that predispose vulnerability include:
  - demographic characteristics, beliefs systems, and social structures variables.

    - These attributes influence vulnerability status

      - They are associated with social position, status, access to resources, health behaviors and variations in health status

Racial / Ethnic Minorities

- In 1997
  - The U.S. Office of Management and Budget (OMB) included race and ethnicity to reflect diversity.

- Minimum categories of race include:
  - black, Asian, American Indian or Alaska Native, Native Hawaiian or Other Pacific Islander and white.

- OMB included 2 ethnicities:
  - Hispanic and Latino

Racial / Ethnic Minorities

- Significant differences exists across the various racial/ethnic groups on health.

  - Minority race and ethnicity usually serves as a proxy for factors such as:

    - socioeconomic status, language ability, or cultural behaviors that are correlated with health status and health care experiences.

  - Racial/ethnic minorities have poorer access, receive poorer-quality care and greater deficits in health status

    - Look at Exhibit 11.2, pages 251 - 252

Racial/Ethnic Minorities

- Consistently over decades of research

  - minorities have poor access to health services compared with white counterparts,

    - even after considering insurance, socioeconomics, and health status.

- The most commonly used measure of access is

  - whether or not a person has a regular or usual source of care

Racial / Ethnic Minorities

- Federal initiatives try to generate national attention on racial disparities in health

  - Look at Exhibit 11.3, page 253

- The Office of Minority Health

  - coordinates federal agencies and the minority health initiatives

    - however, it reflects a somewhat fragmented approach to addressing disparities in minority health and health care.

Notes

Women and Children

- Women in the U. S. enjoy a life expectancy almost eight years longer that of men, but they:
  - have a higher prevalence of health problems over their lifetime
  - develop more acute and chronic illnesses
    - resulting in more short and long-term disabilities
  - have a higher percentage of deaths at all ages for heart disease and stroke
  - have the highest growing population diagnosed with AIDS
  - suffer greater morbidity and poorer health outcomes

- Differences between men and women are equally pronounced for mental illness.

Women and Children

- The Office on Research on Women's Health

  - Administered by the National Institute on Health

    - Under DHHS

    - Has a mission to stimulate, coordinate and implement a comprehensive women's health agenda on research service delivery and education across DHHS and other agencies

Women and Children

- Children's health has unique aspects of delivery such as:
  - developmental vulnerability, dependency, and patterns of morbidity and mortality

- Developmental vulnerability refers to:
  - the rapid and cumulative physical and emotional changes that characterize childhood and the effects that illness, injury, or untoward family and social circumstances can have on a child's life.

Women and Children

- Dependency means
  - the special circumstances children face where others have to recognize and respond to their health needs.

- Children are increasingly affected by "new morbidities" such as:
  - Drug and alcohol abuse
  - Family and neighborhood violence
  - Emotional disorders
  - Learning problems

Geographic Distribution: Rural Health

- Poverty
  - Consistent in rural areas
  - Affects access

- Geographic maldistribution creates a shortage of health care professionals in rural settings
  - another dimension of poor health care delivery.

- Rural populations face greater barriers in access to care.

Geographic Distribution: Rural Health

To improve access in rural America there is:

- The National Health Service Corps

- Health Manpower Shortage Areas

- Medically Underserved Areas

- Community and Migrant Health Centers

- Rural Health Clinics Acts

Notes

Enabling Characteristics

Enabling characteristics include:

– socioeconomic status,

– individual assets, and

– mediating factors

Enabling Characteristics

- Socioeconomic status is associated with
    - social position, access to resources, variations in health status, income, education, employment status and occupation

- Individual assets (human capital) contributes to
    - one's ability to be self-sufficient

- Mediating factors are associated with
    - the use of health care services (e.g. health insurance, access to and quality health care)

Enabling Characteristics

Uninsured tend to:

– be poor and less educated

– work in part-time jobs and/or are employed by small firms

– be younger (25-40)

– be ethnic minorities

Enabling Characteristics

- Homelessness

  - Approximately 26 million (14% of the U.S. population) are homeless at some point in their lives

  - Most live in major urban areas

  - 19% live in rural areas

  - 8% are parents with children

  - 1/3 are veterans of war

  - 20% are women

Notes

Enabling Characteristics

Homelessness

  - The homeless face several barriers to adequate and appropriate health care:
    - financial barriers and
    - problems in satisfying eligibility requirements for health insurance
    - transportation
    - lack of sanitation, a stable place to store medicines,
    - inability to buy/get nutritious food

Enabling Characteristics

- Federal Initiatives to Eliminate Socioeconomic Disparities

  - Programs that have helped eliminate socioeconomic differences:

    - Community Health Center Program
    - National Health Service Corps
    - Public Housing Primary Care Program
    - Health Schools, Health Communities Program
    - Health Care for the Homeless Program

Need Characteristics

- Mental Health

- Chronic Illness / Disability

- HIV / AIDS

Need Characteristics

- Self-perceived or professionally-evaluated health status refers to

  - self-perceived physical and mental health status and diagnoses of disease and illness from a health professional.

Mental Health

- Mental illness ranks second, after ischemic heart disease, as a burden on health and productivity.

  - Mental illness is a risk factor for death from suicide, cardiovascular disease, and cancer.

Mental Health

- Most mental health services are provided in the general medicine sector, rather than through formal mental health specialist services.

  - a concept first describe by Regier and colleagues as the de facto mental health service system

Mental Health

- The nation's mental health system is composed of two subsystem,

  - one primarily for individuals with insurance coverage or private funds and

  - the other for those without private means of coverage.

Chronic Illness / Disability

- Chronic conditions are characterized by persistent and reoccurring health consequences lasting over a long period, which are generally irreversible

- Chronic illness and disability pose unique challenges to a health care system that is primarily oriented towards treating acute illness.

Notes

HIV / AIDS

- Acquired Immunodeficiency Syndrome (AIDS) is caused by
  – the human immunodeficiency virus (HIV).

  – HIV is a retrovirus that
    - causes immune system suppression leading to AIDS.

HIV / AIDS

- Many public health experts believe that cases of AIDS are still underreported.

  – The reason for such underreporting include

    - poor reporting standards in US health department's patients

    - denial of the risk behaviors that are likely to transmit HIV

HIV / AIDS

- Other HIV problems in the United States include issues of urban home health care:

  – HIV infection in rural communities

  – children and women

  – lack of HIV prevention programs

  – discrimination

  – and the need for more HIV/AIDS-related research and health care provider training.

Notes

Chapter 12

Cost, Access,
and Quality

Introduction

- Cost, access, and quality are
  - three major cornerstones of health care delivery.

- An interactive relationship exists between
  - the cost of health care,
  - people's ability to get health care when needed,
  - the quality of services delivered.

Introduction

- Past attempts at universal access have failed

- The premise is that
  - cost and access go hand-in-hand
    - cost and access are primary U.S. concerns

- Quality is increasingly taking center stage

Introduction

- Cost is a factor in quality

- Quality is achieved when accessible services are provided

Cost of Health Care

"Cost"

- has three different meanings or perspectives

  - Price
    - A physician's bill or health care premium

  - Health Care Expenditure or Spending $(P*Q = E)$
    - Reflects the consumption of economic resources in the delivery of care
      - Resources are health insurance, professionals' skills, pharmaceuticals, medical equipment, discoveries

  - Physician's perspective includes
    - Staff salaries, capital, rental, supplies

High in Cost

- Health care spending spiraled upward at double-digit rates during the 1970's

  - following a massive growth in access created by the Medicare and Medicaid programs in 1965

High in Cost

- The rate of growth has again started to accelerate, albeit at a relatively slow pace.

- The main culprits for this recent rise in expenditures are:
  - hospital services,
  - prescription drugs, and
  - physician services.

High in Cost

National health expenditures are evaluated by

- comparing medical inflation to general inflation
  - measured by annual changes in the consumer price index (CPI)

- comparing changes in the national health spending to changes in the GDP.

  - Look at Table 12.1, page 267

Reasons For High Cost

Rising health care expenditures have been attributed to:

- Third-party payment
- Imperfect Market
- Growth of Technology
- Increase in the Elderly Population
- Medical Model of Health Care Delivery
- Multipayer System and Administrative Costs
- Defensive Medicine
- Waste and Abuse
- Practice Variations

Reasons For High Cost

- Third-Party Payment
  - pays the lion's share for most of the services used; not the consumer

- Imperfect Market
  - Utilization of health care is driven by need, not demand

  - Quantity of health care produced is usually higher than in competitive markets

  - Prices are permanently higher than the true cost of production

Reasons For High Cost

- Growth of Technology
  - Growth and intensive use of technology have a direct impact on the escalation of health care cost.

  - Once new technology is developed,
    - it creates demand for its use.

  - Technology raises the expectations of consumers about what medical science can do to diagnose, treat disease and prolong life.

Reasons For High Cost

- Increase in the Elderly Population

  - Elderly consume more health care at 3.5 times the rate

  - With increased life expectancy and the aging of the baby-boomer generation,
    - there are increases in its elderly population.

Reasons For High Cost

- Medical Model of Health Care Delivery

  - The medical model emphasizes medical intervention
    - Prevention is de-emphasized

  - Health promotion and disease prevention have not accorded their place in the US health care delivery system.

Reasons For High Cost

- Multipayer System and Administrative Costs

  - Administrative cost are cost associated with

    - the management of the financing, insurance, delivery, and payment functions, and can include managing enrollment, monitoring utilization, claims processing, denials and appeals, marketing and promotion

  - Administrative costs can amount to about 24-25% of all health expenditures

Reasons For High Cost

- Defensive Medicine

  - Results because the U.S. has many legal risks for providers

  - Leads to tests and service that are
    - not medically justified, but are performed by physicians to protect themselves against malpractice lawsuits.

    - Unrestricted malpractice claims add to health care costs

Reasons For High Cost

- Waste and Abuse

  – Fraud involves
    - a knowing disregard of the truth
      – typically occurs when billing claims or cost reports are intentionally falsified.

  – Fraud is a major problem in Medicare and Medicaid

  – Examples of fraud include:
    - Providing services not medically necessary or billing for a higher-priced service

Reasons For High Cost

- Practice Variations

  – referred to as small area variations
    - it is the differences in practice patterns
      – have been associated with geographic areas of the country
    - they signal gross inefficiencies in the U.S. delivery system
      – they increase costs without better outcomes

Cost Containment

Costs need to be controlled because

  – Americans have to forgo other goods and services

  – economic resources should be directed to their highest valued uses

Cost Containment

- One reason that cost-control efforts in the U.S. have not been successful is

  – Cost shifting

    - providers make up for lost revenues by increasing utilization or

    - charge higher prices in other areas free of controls

Cost Containment

- Health Planning

  – an undertaking by government to align and distribute health care resources that would achieve health outcomes for all

  – Market forces are allowed to govern the system

Cost Containment

- Price Controls

  – One of the most important undertakings to control price for inpatient hospital care was

    - the conversion of hospital Medicare reimbursement from a retrospective to a prospective system

      – based on diagnosis-related groups as authorized under the Social Security Amendments of 1983.

        - costs, however, shifted from inpatient to outpatient

Cost Containment

- Peer Review

  - the process of medial review of utilization and quality carried out by, or under, the supervision of physicians.

  – A new system of peer review organizations (PRO) established whether care was
    - reasonable, necessary, of quality and provided in an appropriate setting

    - they can deny payment if care does not meet with their standards.

  – PROs are also referred to as quality improvement organizations

Cost Containment

- Competitive Approaches

  – Competition is
    - rivalry among sellers for customers.
      – can be in the form of technical quality, amenities, access or other factors

    - in health care delivery, it means that
      – providers of health care services try to attract patients who have the ability to choose from several different providers.

Cost Containment

- Competitive Approaches

  – Demand-side incentives

    - cost-sharing mechanisms that place a larger cost burden on consumers

      – encouraging consumers to be
        - more cost conscious in selecting the insurance plan that best serves their needs and
        - judicious in utilization

Cost Containment

- Competitive Approaches

  - Supply-side regulation

    - antitrust laws in the United States, which prohibit business practices that stifle competition among providers

      - examples include price fixing, price discrimination, exclusive contracting arrangement, and mergers

    - it forces health care organizations to be cost-efficient

Unequal in Access

- Access to care
  - the ability to obtain needed, affordable, convenient, acceptable, and effective personal health services in a timely manner.

- Access is a determinant of
  - health status, environment, lifestyle and heredity factors

Unequal in Access

Data on Access

- Population-based surveys supported by federal statistical agencies are the major data sources for conducting analyses on access to care.

- With managed care,
  - databases are critical in recording and evaluating access

Notes

Unequal in Access

Data on Access

- National Health Interview Survey (NIHS) and Medical Expenditure Panel Survey (MEPS) are both leading data sources used to monitor access trends

- MEPS
  - Consists of surveys that have data on health care use and expenditures such as:
    - inpatient, outpatient, dental care, prescriptions, coverage, access payment sources, health status, disability and demographics
      - Look at Table 12.2, page 277-8

Unequal in Access

Data on Access

- The federal government collects data on
  - community health centers
  - HIV/AIDS, and
  - mental health

- States, associations, and research institutions also collect data on

  - health services utilization, state managed care, etc.

Unequal in Access

Access Disparities

- Both low socioeconomic status and minority group members are associated with lower overall health care usage and access

- Nonwhite persons under age 65 are 5 to 22% less likely to be insured

- Racial/ethnic minorities are less likely than their white counterparts to have a specific source of ongoing care.

- Hispanics are less likely to have a primary care provider

- Nonwhite Medicare beneficiaries have fewer cancer screenings, flu shots and ambulatory visits

Unequal in Access

Reasons for Unequal Access

- Barriers exist at the individual and system levels

- Individual level
  - minority origins, low income, less education, disabilities, chronic illness, uninsured

- Access is predicted by
  - race, income, occupation

Unequal in Access

Access Initiatives

- Sheppard-Towner Act of 1921
  - To provide direct primary care to economically disadvantaged mothers and children

- Social Security Amendments
  - Screening and preventive programs

- Great Society programs
  - Access among disadvantaged populations

- Medicare
  - Cancer screenings and immunizations
  - State Children's Health Insurance Programs (ASCHIPS)

Unequal in Access

- Critique and Prospect

  - It is society's duty to ensure equitable access

  - Scarcity of resources limits access to the poor and those who live in rural areas.
    - surpluses are not shifted to respond to needs

Notes

Average in Quality

Quality indicators can be both:

- Micro-perspectives
  - focuses on services at the point of delivery
  - looks at the performance of an individual or organization

- Macro-perspectives
  - looks at quality from the population's standpoint
  - reflects the performance of the entire health care delivery system

  - Look at Exhibit 12.2, page 282

Average in Quality

The Institute of Medicine defines quality as

- "The degree to which health services for individuals and populations increase the likelihood of desired health outcomes and are consistent with current professional knowledge"

  - leaves out the roles of cost and access in the evaluation of quality

Average in Quality

The Institute of Medicine definition has implications:

1. Quality occurs on a continuum (unacceptable to excellent)

2. The focus is on services provided by the system (not individual behaviors)

3. Quality may be evaluated from the individual or population's perspective

4. Emphasis is on desired health outcomes

5. Professional consensus is used to develop measures of quality

Average in Quality

- Donabedian proposed three domains in which health care quality should be examined

  - Structure

  - Process

  - Outcomes

  - All are important in measuring quality and are complementary—as such, they should be used collectively

    - Look at Figure 12.2, page 285

Average in Quality

- Structure

  - "the relatively stable characteristics of

    - the providers of care,

    - of the tools and resources they have at their disposal,

    - and of the physical and organizational setting in which they work."

Average in Quality

- Process

  - the specific way in which care is provided.

  - Examples:
    - correct diagnostic test,
    - correct prescriptions,
    - accurate drug administration

  - Main developments
    - clinical practice guidelines
    - critical pathways
    - risk management

Average in Quality

- Outcomes

  - the effects or final results obtained from utilizing the structure and processes of health care delivery.

  - viewed as the measure of effectiveness of the health care delivery system.

  - suggests overall improvement in health status

  - measures include:
    - infection rates, rates of rehospitalization, and patient satisfaction

Developments In Process Improvement

- Clinical Practice Guidelines

- Cost-Efficiency

- Critical Pathways

- Risk Management

Developments In Process Improvement

- Clinical Practice Guidelines

  - Also called medical practice guidelines
    - They are preferred clinical processes

  - Constitutes a plan for managing a clinical problem based on evidence

  - To provide protocols to guide physicians' clinical decisions

  - The intention is to lower costs and get better outcomes

Developments In
Process Improvement

- Cost-Efficiency

  - Referred to as
    - Cost effectiveness, cost efficiency

  - Cost efficient when benefits received are greater than the cost incurred

  - This point is optimal quality
    - The demarcation between underutilization and overutilization

Developments In
Process Improvement

- Critical Pathways

  - outcome-based and patient-centered case management tools that are interdisciplinary and facilitate coordination of care among multiple clinical departments and caregivers.

Developments In
Process Improvement

- Critical Pathways

  - A time-line that identifies planned medical interventions along with expected patient outcomes for a diagnosis

Developments In Process Improvement

● Risk Management

    – pro-active efforts to prevent adverse events related to clinical care and facilities operations, focusing on avoiding medical malpractice

Conclusion

● The greatest challenges to health care delivery
    – increasing costs, lack of access, concerns about quality

● Health care costs in the U.S. are highest in the world

● Access is a determinant of health status

Notes

Chapter 13

Health Policy

Introduction

- The United States does not have a centrally controlled system of health care delivery,

  - It does, however have a history of federal, state, and local government involvement in health care and health policy.

What is Health Policy?

- Public policies are
  - authoritative decisions made in the
    - legislative (congressional),
    - executive (presidential), or
    - judicial (Supreme Court) branches of government

  - intended to direct or influence the actions, behaviors, and/or decisions of others.

What is Health Policy?

- Health policies are
  - public policies that
    - pertain to or influence the pursuit of health

- Health policies are
  - the aggregate of
    - principles that distribute resources, services, and political influences that impact the health of the population

What is Health Policy?

- Different Forms of Health Policies

  - Health policies are often byproducts of
    - public social policies enacted by the government.

  - Health policies pertain to health care at all levels,
    - including policies affecting the production, provision, and financing of health care services.

What is Health Policy?

- Different Forms of Health Policies

  - Health policies can affect

    - groups or classes of individuals, such as physicians, the poor, elderly and children.

    - types of organizations, such as medical schools, HMOs, nursing homes, medical technology producers and employers

What is Health Policy?

- Regulatory Tools

  – Call on government to prescribe and control the behavior of a target group by monitoring the group and imposing sanctions if it fails to comply.

What is Health Policy?

- Allocative Tools
  – Involves the direct provision of income, services or goods to a group of individuals or organizations
  – Two main types:

  - Distributive
    – policies spread benefits throughout society.

  - Redistributive
    – Takes money or power from one group and gives it to another
      - therefore health policy can be politically-charged

Principle Features
of US Health Policy

- Government as Subsidiary to the Private Sector

  – It's fragmented,
  – incremental,
  – piece-meal reform,
  – pluralistic (special interest),
  – decentralized role for the states,
  – impact of presidential leadership

  – These features interact or influence the development and evolution of health policy.

Notes

Principle Features of US Health Policy

- Government as Subsidiary to the Private Sector

  - Health care is not seen as a right of citizenship or a primary responsibility of government.
    - The private sector has a dominant role

  - Americans prefer market solutions over government intervention

  - The complexity of health care makes it difficulty for many consumers to make informed decisions

Principle Features of US Health Policy

- Government as Subsidiary to the Private Sector

  - Government has grown incrementally in response to perceived problems and negative consequences

  - Policy interventions begin with the identification of a problem where markets fail or do not function well

Principle Features of US Health Policy

- Government as Subsidiary to the Private Sector

  - Health coverage is a privilege

    - government is left to fill the gap for the most vulnerable of the uninsured population.

Notes

Principle Features
of US Health Policy

• Fragmented, Incremental, and Piecemeal Reform

- The mix of government and private insurance results in a complex and fragmented system of health care financing in which:

  1. The employed are insured by voluntary insurance through contributions that they and their employer pay

  2. The elderly are financed by Social Security tax revenues
     - Medicare Part A and B, Medigaps

Principle Features
of US Health Policy

• Fragmented, Incremental, and Piecemeal Reform

  3. The poor are covered through Medicaid via federal, state, and local revenues

  4. Special populations, such as Veterans, Native Americans, and the armed forces, have coverage provided directly by the federal government.

Principle Features
of US Health Policy

• Pluralistic and Interest Group Politics

- Health policies have been based on interest groups and incremental policies

  • Innovative, nonincremental policies are resisted, because the measures increase threats to interest groups

---

Notes

_____

_____

_____

_____

_____

_____

_____

_____

_____

_____

_____

_____

_____

_____

_____

_____

_____

_____

_____

_____

_____

_____

_____

_____

_____

_____

_____

_____

_____

_____

_____

Principle Features of US Health Policy

- Pluralistic and Interest Group Politics

  - The membership of the policy community has included,
    1. the legislative committees
       -- with jurisdiction in a policy domain,
    2. the executive branch agencies
       -- responsible for implementing policies in the public domain
    3. the interest groups in the private domain

    - The first two are suppliers of policies demanded by the third.

Principle Features of US Health Policy

- Pluralistic and Interest Group Politics

  - Interest Groups
    - Most effective demanders of policies
    - Adamant about resisting any major change
    - They combine and concentrate the resources of their members
    - Examples of health care interest groups:
      - American Medical Association (AMA),
      - American Association of Retired Persons (AARP)
      - American Hospital Association

Principle Features of US Health Policy

- Pluralistic and Interest Group Politics

  - Employers

    - Their concerns are about health insurance benefits for their
      - employees, dependents, and retirees

    - Most small businesses oppose mandates of coverage because of the cost

Principle Features of US Health Policy

- Pluralistic and Interest Group Politics

  - Consumer Groups

    - The interests of consumers are not uniform

    - Consumers do not have sufficient financial means to organize and advocate for their own best interests.

Principle Features of US Health Policy

- Pluralistic and Interest Group Politics

  - Manufacturers of Technology

    - Health policy concerns regarding medical technology include:

      1. Its role in health costs

      2. Its health benefits to people (although not always)

Principle Features of US Health Policy

- Pluralistic and Interest Group Politics
  - Alliances
    - To overcome pluralistic interests and maximize policy outcome, diverse interest groups form
      - alliances among themselves and with members of the legislative body to
        - protect and enhance the interests of those receiving benefits from government programs.
    - Each member of the alliance receives benefits

Notes

_____

_____

_____

_____

_____

_____

_____

_____

_____

_____

_____

_____

_____

_____

_____

_____

_____

_____

_____

_____

_____

_____

_____

_____

_____

_____

_____

_____

_____

_____

_____

Principle Features of US Health Policy

- Decentralized Role of the States

  - States develop and implement health policies involving:
    1. Financial support (care and treatment) for the poor and disabled
       - Medicaid, SCHIP
    - Quality assurance, practitioner and facility oversight
       - Licensure and regulation
    - Regulation of health care costs and insurance carriers
    - Health personnel training
    - Authorization of local government health services

Principle Features of US Health Policy

- Decentralized Role of the States

  - States have broad, legal authority to regulate the health care system.

  - The state can:
    - license and regulate health care facilities and professionals
    - restrict the content, marketing, and price of health insurance
    - set and enforce environmental quality standards
    - enact controls on health care costs

Principle Features of US Health Policy

- Decentralized Role of the States

  - States finance much of the health care for the poor

  - Most incremental policy actions originate at the state level

  - State-initiated programs address vulnerable populations

  - Some argue there is too much state control over health policy decisions

Principle Features
of US Health Policy

- Impact of Presidential Leadership

  - Americans look to presidential leadership for major change in health policies

  - Presidents can influence outcomes through compromises

    - Lyndon B. Johnson helped pass
      - Medicare and Medicaid

    - Harry Truman helped pass the
      - Hill-Burton Hospital Construction Act

Development of
Legislative Health Policy

- Policy Cycle

  - Making health policy is a complex process

    - It involves both private and public sectors, including multiple levels of government

Development of
Legislative Health Policy

- Policy Cycle

  - The formation and implementation of health policy occurs in a policy cycle comprising five components:

    1. issue raising
    2. policy design
    3. building of public support
    4. legislative decision making and building of policy support and,
    5. policy implementation

  - These activities are shared by Congress and interest groups

Notes

Development of
Legislative Health Policy

- Legislative Process

  - A bill is introduced in the House of Representatives,
    - it is assigned to a committee by the Speaker
    - it is reassigned to a subcommittee
      - It is sent to agencies to hold hearings ("markups") to get testimony and possible amendments

      - Committees and subcommittees may "recommend," "not recommend" or "table" the bill

  - The full House hears the bill, at which point they may (further) amend it. If it is approved, they send it to the Senate

Development of
Legislative Health Policy

- Legislative Process

  - The Senate follows the same process as the House,
    - however, if amendments are added in the Senate, it goes back to the House for approval

  - After the bill has passed in both the House and Senate in identical form, it is forwarded to the president for signature.

  - If the president signs the legislation, it becomes law

Development of
Legislative Health Policy

- Legislative Process

  - Once legislation is signed into law, it is forwarded to the appropriate agency for implementation

  - The new regulation is posted in the Federal Register
    - Hearings are held to see how the law will be implemented

  - The bureaucracy publishes, gathers comments and rewrites regulations

  - The program goes to 50 states for enabling legislation (if appropriate)

  - Local interests begin a new political process to shape the final outcome

Critical Policy Issues

- Access to Care
  - Providers
  - Public Financing
  - Access and the Elderly
  - Access and Minorities
  - Access in Rural Areas
  - Access and Low Income
  - Access and Persons with AIDS

- Cost Containment

- Quality of Care
  - Research and Policy Development

Critical Policy Issues

- Government health policies are enacted to
  - Resolve or prevent deficiencies in health care delivery

- Health care has been focusing on:

  - Access to care
    - Expanding insurance coverage, outreach to rural areas

  - Cost of care
    - PPS, RBRVS

  - Quality of care
    - AHRQ and clinical practice guidelines

Critical Policy Issues

- Access to Care

  - Policies on access are aimed primarily at

    - providers and financing mechanisms,

      - with the purpose of expanding care to the most needy and underserved populations (i.e., the elderly, minorities, rural residents, those with low incomes, and persons with AIDS)

Notes

Critical Policy Issues

Access to Care

Providers

- Policy helps to ensure that there are enough providers and that their geographic distribution is desirable.
- The supply of physicians is a policy issue that could influence people entering the medical profession
  - entrance to medical professions are influenced by government assistance and grants

Critical Policy Issues

Access to Care

Providers

- Policy has expanded to include:
  - The National Health Service Corp
  - Legislation supporting rural health clinics to expand access
  - Student assistance programs to emergency medical services
  - Establishment of community health centers in inner cities and rural towns

Critical Policy Issues

Access to Care

Public Financing

- Many see national health care as the best way to ensure access.
  - the U.S., however focuses on certain groups

- Medicare and Medicaid
  - established the precedent that government should facilitate access to health care among those unable to secure it for themselves.

Critical Policy Issues

- Access to Care
  - Access and the Elderly
    - Two main concerns about the Medicare policy

      1. Spending must be restrained to keep the program viable.

      2. The program must be made comprehensive by adding services not currently covered or covered inadequately.
         (i.e., nursing home coverage)

Critical Policy Issues

- Access to Care

  - Access and Minorities

    - Minorities are more likely than whites to face access problems.
    - Low income, minority status, cultural habits cause access problems
    - Policies should encourage
      - sensitivity programs to the special needs of minorities, and
      - delivery of services to areas populated by minorities

Critical Policy Issues

- Access to Care

  - Access in Rural Area

    - In rural communities, making medical care available to residents is difficult, because most health care organizations are established in more urban areas

    - The National Health Service Corps helps address personnel shortages in rural areas, but only for a limited time

    - Programs to create incentives for permanent practices in rural areas are needed

Critical Policy Issues

- Access to Care

  - Access and Low Income
    - Low-income mothers and their children have problems accessing the health care system because
      - they lack insurance and generally live in medically underserved areas.
      - they are also less likely to receive prenatal care

    - SCHIP
      - Federal funds with some state-flexibility--target health care coverage for children

Critical Policy Issues

- Access to Care

  - Access and Person with AIDS
    - Persons with AIDS and those who have HIV have problems obtaining health care.
    - AIDS patients have difficulty getting insurance
      - Their disease process leads to catastrophic expenses
    - Financial access can be a barrier
    - AIDS is a challenge to policymakers committed to universal access

Critical Policy Issues

- Cost Containment

  - The strengths of the U.S. health care system contribute to its weaknesses.
  - The U.S. has the latest technology and well-trained specialists
    - This leads to the most expensive means of providing health care in the world
  - Two major policy initiatives enacted by the federal government to contain costs have targeted
    - Hospitals with PPS, and
    - Physicians' services with RBRVS

Critical Policy Issues

● Cost Containment

– The National Health Planning and Resources Development Act of 1974 became law in 1975.

  • This act marked the transition from improvement of access to cost containment as the principle theme in federal health policy.

    – Health planning through a CON review was a policy tool to contain costs

Critical Policy Issues

● Quality of Care

– Along with access and cost, quality of care is the third main concern of health care policy.

– The Health Care Quality Act of 1986

  • Legislation that mandated the collection of national data on legal actions against health care providers

  • This information allows people to know actions brought against physicians in other states

Critical Policy Issues

● Quality of Care

– Agency for Healthcare Research and Quality (AHRQ)

  • is to conduct and support research on outcomes, effectiveness, and appropriateness of health care services and procedures
  • funds patient outcomes research teams (PORTS):
    – that focuses on certain medical conditions
    – that are part of the medical treatment effectiveness program which has 4 elements:
      1. Medical treatment effectiveness research
      2. Development of databases for research
      3. Development of clinical guidelines
      4. Dissemination of research findings and clinical guidelines

Notes

Critical Policy Issues

- Quality of Care
  - Research and Policy Development
    - Research can influence health policy through
      - documentation,
        - gathering, cataloging, and correlating
      - analysis
        - program evaluation and outcomes research
      - prescription
        - a course of action that has a desirable consequence

Conclusion

- Health policies are developed to serve the public's interest

- National health care is supported, but the idea of federal government running the system is not preferred

- The challenge is:
  - finding a balance between government provisions and control, and the market to improve coverage and affordability

Notes

Chapter 14

The Future of
Health
Services
Delivery

Introduction

- Are we close to a national health care system in the United States?

    - Americans tend not to favor because
        - it is contrary to the beliefs and values prevalent
        - they want less government in private affairs
        - they are disenchanted with national initiatives
        - the middle class does not want to pay higher taxes

- However, the rising numbers of uninsured plague our society

Introduction

- Other developed countries with universal coverage try to stay solvent

- U.S. leads in technology innovation
    - Other countries later adopt our technology
        - Does the U.S. then subsidize health care for other countries?

- America has a large share of immigrants
    - Their costs for care are passed onto citizens

Introduction

- Managed care helped slow down the growth of health care expenditures by
  - utilization review and reduced reimbursement
    - without declines in quality

- Backlashes occurred because there was
  - an erosion of choice
  - restrictions in direct access to specialists
  - limited reimbursement to providers
  - control by managed care companies over physicians' utilization

- HMOs responded by offering:
  - Health Maintenance Organizations (HMO)
  - Preferred Provider Organizations (PPO)
  - Point-of-Service (POS)

Introduction

- Relaxed controls and flexibility puts managed care at a crossroads again

- Beginning in 2001
  - premiums began to rise at unsustainable rates

- Between 2002-2003
  - monthly premiums for employer-sponsored plans rose almost 14%

Future of Managed Care, Health Care Costs, and System Reform

- Managed care is a mature industry in the U.S.
  - 90% of private insured people
  - 50% of Medicaid beneficiaries
    - are enrolled into managed care plans

- Forces prevent the reduction of health care excesses
  - so the cost continues to rise

- The gap between health care costs and premium increases cannot be sustained
  - Look at Figure 14.1, page 317

Future of Managed Care, Health Care Costs, and System Reform

- The aging population is a factor for the future
  - By 2013, health care will consume 18.4% of the gross domestic product
  - The elderly use more health care

- With rising health care costs, the following items will continue to fall through the cracks:
  - utilization management
  - reimbursement issues
  - prescription drug benefits
  - quality measures
  - the plight of the uninsured

Trends in Health Insurance

➢ Defined-Benefit to Defined-Contribution Plans

- Medical Savings Accounts

- Tax Credits

- High Risk Pools

Trends in Health Insurance

- Defined benefit plan
  - most employers offer this plan
  - the employer pre-selects one or more health plans
  - consumers have no financial incentives to be prudent buyers
  - patients are mostly removed from the cost of care
  - in the future, consumers will likely bear more responsibility
➢ Defined contribution plans
  - employers commit to a fixed dollar for benefits
  - the fixed dollar amount is paid to the employee, who then pays for a health care plan they select
  - used for retirement benefits
  - gives employees a greater role in buying health insurance and services
  - can work hand-in-hand with a medical savings account (MSA)

Notes

Trends in Health Insurance

➢ Medical Savings Plans (MSAs)
  ➢ is an employee-managed savings account with a high deductible catastrophic health insurance plan
    ➢ the high deductible helps keep premiums law
    ➢ catastrophic plans do not cover routine and inexpensive health care services, but for major expenses beyond the deductible
  ➢ are funded with pre-tax dollars contributed by the employer and employees
  ➢ allow the balance to roll over to next year
  ➢ are used to pay out-of-pocket health care expenses
    ➢ including insurance premiums, deductibles and copayments
  ➢ promote individual responsibility in buying health insurance plans

Trends in Health Insurance

Tax Credits

  ➢ Will President George W. Bush's proposal to introduce tax credits allow Americans to buy health insurance?
    ➢ it may help improve
      ➢ the functioning of private markets
      ➢ the empowerment of patients to make informed decisions
      ➢ the use of high-value health care, reducing utilization
    ➢ can be in the form of vouchers to enable poor to buy insurance

    ➢ those who are high-risk may be left uninsured

Trends in Health Insurance

➢ High Risk Pools
  ➢ target groups who cannot buy health insurance because of their poor health
  ➢ are in about 30 states with high-risk pools that subsidize coverage
  ➢ have premium rates are capped at 25% to 50% of the average market rate
  ➢ have deductibles that are about $1,000 or less with an 80:20 coinsurance

Notes

Options for Comprehensive Reform

- Single-payer

- Managed competition

- Play-or-Pay

- Employer mandates

Options for Comprehensive Reform

Single-Payer

- The closet approach to Canada's system
- It places the financing with one entity,
  - usually the federal government
- Advantages include:
  - All Americans, lawful residents are entitled to benefits regardless of income
  - Medicaid, Medicare, Tricare and the Federal Employee Health Benefits Program would no longer be necessary
- Private insurance would still exist for those who want coverage beyond the basic government plan
- Providers would be reimbursed on a fee-for-service with a government scale
- Hospitals, nursing homes, other facilities would have an annual prospective budget to provide all care

Options for Comprehensive Reform

- Managed Competition

  - Clinton's universal plan was based on managed competition

  - Every citizen would have a comprehensive package

  - It would be competition between
    - purchasing cooperatives and managed care plans

Options for Comprehensive Reform

- Play-or-Pay

  – Employer-based
    - employers must provide health insurance for employees (play) or pay into public health insurance

    - If employer chooses to pay, financing is paid by a payroll tax
      – paid by the employer and employee
        - like Medicare and Social Security is paid

    - The payroll deduction system is already in place
      – so there would be little disruption in the process

Options for Comprehensive Reform

- Employer Mandate
  – Requires employers to help pay for employee coverage

    - Hawaii is the only state that has implemented this system
      – it was in place before the Employee Retirement Income Security Act (ERISA) ws enacted
        - The ERISA exempts self-insured business from state insurance regulations and taxes
        - ERISA prohibits employer mandates

    - There is opposition by employers
      – especially small businesses

National and Global Challenges

- Wellness, Prevention and Health Promotion

- Chronic Illnesses

- Infectious Diseases and Globalization

National & Global Challenges

● Wellness, Prevention and Health Promotion

   – Emphasis will move to preventative care from acute

      • helps to keep costs under control

      • a long-run benefit

      • identifies employees' high risk behavior and implements plans

---

National & Global Challenges

Challenges of Chronic Illnesses

   – The U.S. and other nations have improved health status and life expectancy by conquering communicable disease

   – With life expectancy
      • chronic disorders are the major causes of death (i.e., heart disease, lung cancer)

   – The chronically ill face barriers of:
      • affordability and access

National & Global Challenges

Challenges of Chronic Illnesses
   – The system will have to adapt to
      – patient education
      – self-coping skills
      – computerized tracking
      – reminder systems
      – follow-ups
      – promotion of healthy aging

   – To change the system
      • reimbursements have to pay providers for the new services
      • health care professions need training in chronic illnesses

Notes

National & Global Challenges

- Infectious Disease and Globalization

    - Examples include:
        - AIDS
        - Bacterial infections
            - Lyme
            - Antibiotic-resistant bacterias
            - New forms of influenza viruses
        - West Nile virus

    - There is a need to link the nation's foreign and public health policies

Bioterrorism & Transformation of Public Health

- Medical establishments have relegated public health as "unimportant"

- However, Homeland security created a new respect and recognizes public health

- Public Health agencies need to forge partnerships with communities and all levels of government

Future of the Health Care Workforce

- Supply of Physicians and Nurses

- Training in Geriatrics

- Workforce Diversity

Future of the Health Care Workforce

Supply of Physicians and Nurses

- U.S. has a surplus of physicians
  - the need for generalists will remain stable
  - compounds the imbalance between generalists and specialists
- Nursing shortages have been cyclical
  - The Institute for the Future (2002) indicates that
    - the future supply of registered nurses (RNs) will be sufficient to respond to increased demands
  - Demand for Nurse Practitioners is expected to increase
    - they are needed in rural and underserved areas

Future of the Health Care Workforce

- Geriatric Training

  - There is a shortage of
    - workers trained in geriatrics
    - faculty in colleges and universities specializing in geriatrics

  - Elderly use:
    - most of the home health and nursing care services
    - about 50% of hospital inpatient days
    - 25% of all ambulatory care services

Future of the Health Care Workforce

- Workforce Diversity

  - Women continue to enter the workforce in large numbers
    - Some benefits may need to be added (i.e., day care services, flexible work schedules)
  - Nonwhites make up an increasing proportion of the workforce
    - especially in populated cities
    - the workplace will be more diverse, both ethnically and racially
  - Development of cultural competence is needed
    - cultural competence refers to knowledge, skills and attitudes

Notes

Frontiers in Technology

- Clinical Technology

- Information Technology

- Telematics

Frontiers in Technology

Clinical Technology

- rational drug design
- imaging technologies
- minimally invasive surgery
- genetic mapping
- gene therapy
- vaccines
- artificial blood
- xenotransplantation

Frontiers in Technology

Information Technology

- Needed to ensure continuity of patient information

  - providers, intermediaries, and consumers will have to share information

    - it increases communication on administrative issues, such as:
      - eligibility verification
      - approvals for service
      - claims processing

Frontiers in Technology

Telematics

– referred to as telemetry

- combines information and communication technologies

- can expand into isolated areas and people's homes

- can monitor vitals, blood pressure and glucose levels from remote sites with wireless systems

- also includes teleconferences for educational purposes

Conclusion

- Change is coming

- Lack of access and cost inflation will continue to plague the system

- Employers will shift the cost more to employees

- Managed care will have to evolve

- Wellness and Public Health will be more strongly emphasized

- There will be a decline in inpatient hospital care, affecting the workforce

- New frontiers will open with the use of new technologies